Life Skills Literacy

Things to Know About Community Resources

by Richard S. Kimball
illustrated by
Jennifer DeCristoforo

J. WESTON

PUBLISHER
Portland, Maine

D1223843

User's Guide
to
Walch Reproducible Books

As part of our general effort to provide educational materials that are as practical and economical as possible, we have designated this publication a "reproducible book." The designation means that purchase of the book includes purchase of the right to limited reproduction of all pages on which this symbol appears:

Here is the basic Walch policy: We grant to individual purchasers of this book the right to make sufficient copies of reproducible pages for use by all students of a single teacher. This permission is limited to a single teacher, and does not apply to entire schools or school systems, so institutions purchasing the book should pass the permission on to a single teacher. Copying of the book or its parts for resale is prohibited.

Any questions regarding this policy or requests to purchase further reproduction rights should be addressed to:

Permissions Editor
J. Weston Walch, Publisher
321 Valley Street • P. O. Box 658
Portland, Maine 04104-0658

1   2   3   4   5   6   7   8   9   10
ISBN 0-8251-4274-1

Contents

To the Teacher

Things to Know About Community Resources is another title in the growing *Life Skills Literacy* series from J. Weston Walch, Publisher. *Things to Know* books are reproducible, thematic compilations of information aimed at youth and adult English language learners, including ESL students new to American or Canadian culture. These books are intended to help build vocabulary, expand culturally based knowledge, and develop real-life and survival skills. *Things to Know* books include interactive, authentic, cooperative, and idiomatic materials and activities. The books lead to success with language and success in the classroom, the family, and the community.

The *Life Skills Literacy* series is appropriate for ESL learners at intermediate levels and for native learners reading at the fourth-grade level and higher. Each book in the series contains vocabulary lists with nearly 400 words and phrases; in this volume, most words are specifically related to community resources. Illustrative and contextual clues offer assistance with lexical development. Verb forms are generally simple, and the use of passive voice is limited.

The activities in *Things to Know About Community Resources* and its companion books can help individual students build reading and writing proficiencies. They can help full classes and small groups of students develop speaking and listening competencies as well. They can help all learners understand community issues and explore related subjects like government structure and civic responsibility.

Their brevity and focus make *Things to Know* titles excellent resources for tutors working with individual students, whether or not the books are also used in the classroom. Their basic level makes *Things to Know* suitable for a wide range of circumstances and student abilities. Their controlled language and high-interest topics give them appeal for students as well as teachers.

Like other books in the series, this one devotes three pages to each of 24 lessons. The first page of each lesson is for teachers. It provides information and suggestions ranging from general concept considerations to specific Internet sites you and your students might visit. The second and third pages of each lesson are reproducible, for student use. The second page presents topic information and a dialogue, story, or student challenge relating to the information. The third page includes a word list, plus writing and discussion activities for individual, small group, and full-class use.

This book cannot cover all the vocabulary and topics related to community issues students might face. Nor can it be designed to be exactly at the level of each and every student. But it can be—and is—very flexible, covering the basics at a consistently low reading level and then offering numerous ideas for moving beyond. It also provides extension activities to meet a wide range of classroom and personal needs. General ideas for use and adaptation of the materials appear on the following page of Teaching Suggestions. More specific suggestions can be found on the teacher page provided with each lesson.

We believe you will find the Walch *Life Skills Literacy* series and its individual *Things to Know* titles useful with many different students in many different settings. We'll be pleased to hear how well it works for you, to know what other titles you think should be added, and—as always—to learn what more this company can do to serve you and your students.

—*J. Weston Walch, Publisher*

Teaching Suggestions

You can use *Things to Know About Community Resources* basically as is, having learners work through the two reproducible pages of each lesson in one or two class sessions. Or you can make this book the core of a broader approach to community issues by following the many suggestions in the topical teacher pages and expanding each lesson to cover several sessions.

The first step in deciding how to use these pages is, of course, assessing the needs, interests, and abilities of your learners. The second step is considering the characteristics of your own students and community. Wherever you teach, you'll find that your classes benefit most when knowledge of personal needs and local conditions is added to the *Things to Know* mix.

The "Preparation possibilities" on the teacher pages provide some ideas of what you might wish to do in advance to enrich your classes, particularly if you are presenting a topic over several class sessions. But these pages are designed for immediate use, and you need not spend hours preparing for their presentation. If you think local information will be helpful to your groups, follow the suggestions of the teacher pages and assign students to do the research. They will become true learners—and enjoy themselves as well—when they discover the practical value of outside projects. Or invite outsiders to join the class and talk about such complex matters as the court system.

Some of the "Technology resources" listed on the teacher pages assume an Internet connection and use of a search engine like Yahoo!® to look for information and suggested Web pages. Use the topics suggested as your search terms to yield the best results.

The word lists on the third page of each lesson contain between 12 and 15 terms each. Terms referring to resources like the Internet avoid the highly technical and should interest all learners, whatever their backgrounds and concerns. The more general terms are all important to the passages in which they occur. They have been selected with reference to readability levels and vocabulary frequency-use studies. In some cases, you may want to adjust the lists to help meet the needs and interests of your own students. You can underline the words you wish to stress, tape over those you don't want, and add others you find useful. However, be careful not to eliminate terms required for the fill-in sentences that follow.

The idioms and slang and the "fascinating facts" given in the teacher pages are presented as fun and informative extras for some classes. If you use the idioms and slang, consider asking students to try them in sentences and to share other terms they know. You can treat the word lists in the same way, if you like, asking students to build sentences around them and to supply related vocabulary that interests them.

All materials on the activity pages have been prepared with references to varied thinking skills, learning styles, and the several intelligences proposed by Howard Gardner and others. But no mix can be perfect for every class, and these also can—and should—be adjusted to meet the needs of your own groups. The role-plays based on dialogues, stories, and challenges are useful examples. Some students with very limited language skills will benefit from working in pairs and reading dialogues aloud to each other. More advanced students will enjoy and benefit from more creative approaches in which they make up their own parts and decide what might happen next to the characters in the story.

Lesson 1: About Community

Themes:

- Types of community
- The shared resources offered by communities

Background notes: This first lesson offers learners an initial understanding of what communities are, why they exist, and how they offer members an opportunity to share resources. The next two lessons in the book provide overviews of both governmental and private communities. Together, the first three lessons should give learners a good starting point for exploring the wide range of communities found in western society, and for considering the many ways in which they may both benefit from and contribute to those communities.

Preparation possibilities:

- <u>Think about</u>: The various communities in your area and in your students' lives
- <u>Bring to class</u>: Clippings about interesting communities in your area; newspapers and or phone books for student reference (see "Projects to assign learners," below)

Technology resources:

- Search topics: *Community, community resources, community service*
- Web pages to try: Impact Online, FedWorld Information Network

Student pages:

- Page 2 includes: An introduction to communities, with part of John Donne's statement that "no man is an Island, entire of it self"; a dialogue in which two friends discuss communities
- Page 3 includes: A word list you may adjust for your class, and student activities

Especially for ESL: Having ESL students in your class may give you an opportunity to explore the concept of choice in joining communities. Note that the natives of a national community are automatic members of that community. Immigrants, however, may choose to join it. <u>Ask</u>: What is the word for "community" in your first language? Does it cover both government and private organizations?

Extra idioms and slang to introduce:

- *Sign up:* join something
- *Welcome to the club:* join somebody (the speaker) in having a particular problem

Thoughts to share with learners: Some communities—such as towns—are organized; other communities are not. Some people talk about a "community of writers," for example. That just refers to people who write a lot, not an actual club or other organization. Writers don't have to join anything to be part of this community.

Questions to ask learners: What do people mean when they say there is "strength in numbers?" Can you think of a way to show that? (If you bend one small stick or pencil, you can break it easily. But if you put a whole group of sticks or pencils together, you can't break them at all. Is that like people?)

Projects to assign learners: Look through a newspaper or a phone book. How many communities do they talk about? Can you count them all? Share what you find with your class.

A fascinating fact to share: Millions of ants sometimes live in communities together. They share resources like food and space and water. They also share jobs, such as getting food and fighting enemies.

Name_____ Date_____

Lesson 1: About Community

"No man is an **island**." That is a famous **quote**. It means that nobody can live completely alone. We all need other people. Two people together can do a lot more than one. And many people together can do much more than that. So we all join in **communities**. Those are groups of people with something **in common**. In these groups we can help each other. We can also help ourselves. We can have lots of fun, too. People aren't islands. We can't live all alone. And most of us don't want to.

Dialogue: The party

First Friend: Are you going to the **costume** party on Saturday?

Second Friend: Yes. I'm going to wear a **spider** costume.

FF: That's funny. What made you think of that?

SF: I watched a spider making a **web** the other day. "My life is like that web," I thought. "I live in the middle, and I **connect** to lots of other things."

FF: Like your family and friends?

SF: And people at work. And more people at school. It's as if I have different webs in different places.

FF: I see what you mean. But connections make me think of communities. I think you are in a bunch of different communities.

SF: But this town is the only community I live in. I'm not rich. I don't have houses all over the place.

FF: That's not what I mean. Towns and cities are just one kind of community. There are lots of other kinds. And they don't all have **governments**. A community is any group of people connected in some way. Usually

they help people share **resources** of some kinds. In towns, **for example**, people share schools. And some communities, like towns, are public. Others, like **clubs**, are **private**.

SF: I suppose that even my family is a community.

FF: Yes. That's one you get into **automatically**. Like your country. You are born into that.

SF: Right. And I get into others, like my work, by **choice**. But anyway, what are you wearing on Saturday?

FF: I think I'll go as an ant or a bee.

SF: Why?

FF: Talking about community makes me think of ants and bees. They both live and work in their own communities with other ants and bees.

SF: That sounds like fun. But I've got some advice. If you go as an ant or a bee, watch out for spider webs!

2

Life Skills Literacy:
Things to Know About Community Resources

Name _____ Date _____

Lesson 1: About Community

ACTIVITY PAGE

Word List

island	in common	web	resource(s)	private
quote	costume	connect	for example	automatically
communities(y)	spider	government(s)	club(s)	choice

Increasing Your Understanding

1. Look at the word list in the box above. If you don't know a word, find out what it means. Try to figure it out from the way it is used on page 2. Or look it up in a dictionary.

2. Supply the missing word in each of the sentences below. Use the word list above.

   (a) People in communities have something _____, says the paragraph at the top of page 2.

   (b) "No man is an _____," according to a famous quote.

   (c) In the story on page 2, the first friend says that all communities don't have _____.

   (d) The second friend is going to wear a _____ costume to the party.

   (e) "My life is like that web," says the second friend. "I _____ to lots of other things."

Questions to Discuss

1. The first friend talks about different kinds of communities on page 2. What are they? Which ones do people join automatically? Which ones do they join by choice?

2. What are some other kinds of communities? What kinds of resources do the people in them share? Brainstorm your answers.

3. Can you live all alone? What if you landed on an island all alone? What would that be like? Could you live? For how long?

Things to Write About

1. Think of an important community in your life. Write a paragraph about it. What kind of resources does it have?

2. What are two communities you joined automatically? What are two you chose to join? Write a sentence about each one.

Things to Do

1. Act out the story on page 2 with a partner. Use your own words if you want. Talk about how the friends can make their costumes.

2. What does the "web" of your life look like? Draw a spider web. Put yourself in a circle at the center. Use some other circles to show the people and places you are connected with. Then see if some of your classmates have the same circles in their webs.

3. Work with two or three classmates. Think of a story that shows why communities are important. The story can be something you read or saw on TV. Or it can be something you make up. Share your story with the class.

4. Look near your school. What communities do you see? Do they have resources to share? Talk in class about what you find.

3

Life Skills Literacy:
Things to Know About Community Resources

Lesson 2: Government Resources

Themes:

- Levels of government
- Government-based community resources

Background notes: The various government bodies of the United States and Canada provide innumerable resources and services for their populations. But some are little known, and others are hard to find. These pages introduce learners to the several levels of government and some of the resources they offer. Extension activities ask learners to look around and find resources available to them through various government offices. You might wish to consider a field trip to a local government resource, federal building, or state agency. (See also Number 4 under "Things to Do" on page 6.)

Preparation possibilities:

- <u>Think about</u>: The government resources your students may use or wish to use
- <u>Bring to class</u>: Listings of government services available locally

Technology resources:

- Search topics: *Government services, public services*
- Web pages to try: Jobs in Government, Council for Government Reform (and specific government bodies at every level)

Student pages:

- Page 5 includes: A diagram and explanation of government levels; a story in which friends talk about the nature of one state's government
- Page 6 includes: A word list you may adjust for your class, and student activities

Especially for ESL: <u>Ask</u>: What resources do people get from the government in your first country? Are they different from the resources you can get in this country?

Extra idioms and slang to introduce:

- *Uncle Sam:* the U.S. government
- *Dig up:* find

Thoughts to share with learners: The three branches of state government mentioned in the story on page 5 can also be found at the local and national levels. The Internet is a good way to look for government resources. Some books are also very helpful. One example is *Washington Information Digest* (published by Congressional Quarterly).

Questions to ask learners: How are the governments of different states or provinces alike? How are they different? What are some ways you can find out about the community resources governments offer? Is government as confusing as Tara thinks in the story on page 5?

Projects to assign learners: Visit a government building. It might be a town hall, a federal court, or another kind. Look around and see what services and resources people can find there. Share what you learn with your classmates.

A fascinating fact to share: Governments are major employers. In 1998, 25 million Americans had or were looking for government jobs. That's according to Jobs in Government, an Internet site.

Lesson 2: Government Resources

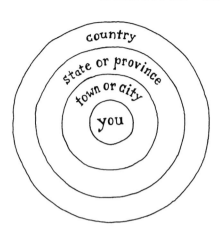

This **diagram** shows you and the circles of government. You are in the middle, and you are in a town. That's a low **level** of government. Then comes the state or province. Next is the nation. Each level has its own **jurisdiction**. That's what it controls. The nation runs the whole country. Does that make it most important? In some ways, yes. But the levels do different jobs. They share power. They offer different resources you might use. So they are all important.

Story: The visit

"Want to go out?" Lodi asked Tara. "There's a good movie downtown."

"I can't," said Tara. "Come see what I'm making."

Tara was working on a large piece of paper covered with lines. "I'm **impressed**," said Lodi. "But what is it?"

"Maybe you're impressed," Tara told him. "But I'm **confused**. My class went to the state **capital** yesterday. Now I have to draw a diagram that shows the parts of the government. I also have to show the resources that some of the parts offer people. Can you understand the lines?"

Lodi looked carefully at Tara's work. "What's that little box at the top?" he asked.

"That's for the state flag. I'm using it as a **symbol** for the whole state. I'll color it in when I'm done with everything else."

"Then I understand what you've done so far. You show three parts of the government. One is the **executive**. That's got people like the **governor** in it. These are the people who carry out the

state's laws. The second part is the **legislature**. It makes new laws. And the third part is the **judiciary**. It runs the state **courts**."

"Right. Now I've got to show some of the things in each branch. Things like **agencies** and **authorities**. That's why I'm confused. The state government is a huge **bureaucracy**."

"Just be glad that you don't have to diagram the federal government," said Lodi.

"I am." Tara picked up her pen and started to add another line. Then she stopped. "Whoops," she said. "I think I'll go to the movie after all."

"Why?"

"I just ran out of ink. I can get another pen on the way to the movies."

"Sounds good."

"I just hope one pen is enough. There may not be enough ink in the whole world to draw in every piece of our state's government."

Life Skills Literacy:
Things to Know About Community Resources

Name_____ Date _____

Lesson 2: Government Resources

Word List

diagram	impress(ed)	symbol	legislature	agencies(y)
level	confuse(d)	executive	judiciary	authorities(y)
jurisdiction	capital	governor	court(s)	bureaucracy

Increasing Your Understanding

1. Look at the word list in the box above. If you don't know a word, find out what it means. Try to figure it out from the way it is used on page 5. Or look it up in a dictionary.

2. Supply the missing word(s) in each of the sentences below. Use the word list above.

   (a) Tara will use a flag as a _____ for her state in the story on page 5.

   (b) "The state government is a huge _____," she says to Lodi.

   (c) Lodi says that the three parts of government are the _____, the _____, and the _____.

   (d) The _____ at the top of page 5 shows you and the circles of government.

   (e) Each government level has its own _____, says the paragraph at the top of page 5.

Questions to Discuss

1. Is Tara right in the story on page 5? Are state and provincial governments confusing? What about local governments? National governments?

2. What are some government resources you might use? What level of government offers them? Brainstorm your answers.

3. Can the diagram on page 5 be larger? Are there other levels of government? What are they?

Things to Write About

1. What does one level of government do for you? Choose one level of government. (Local, national, or state or provincial) Write a paragraph saying how it helps you.

2. What kind of government job would be good? Imagine that you can have a government job helping people. What will it be? What will you do? Think of two jobs you

might like. Write two or three sentences about each of them.

Things to Do

1. Act out the story on page 5 with a partner. Use your own names and words if you want. Talk about some other things that Tara's diagram might show.

2. What does Tara's diagram look like? Read the story on page 5 again. Then draw the beginning of Tara's diagram. See if your classmates have the same ideas. (There isn't any one right way to do this.)

3. What are the most important things national governments do for their people? Work with two or three classmates and list at least five important things. Then share your ideas with the whole class.

4. What kinds of government resources are near you? Look around near your school and home. Share what you find with your class.

Life Skills Literacy:
Things to Know About Community Resources

Lesson 3: Private Resources

Themes:

- Privately funded community resources
- Discovering resources of personal interest

Background notes: Private community resources? The term sounds oxymoronic, but it's an accurate description for many forms of assistance available to all individuals in the United States, Canada, and other countries. In fact, the dichotomy of public and private resources is basic to American society, with responsibilities shifting between the two forms as the tides of philosophy and politics change. These pages complete the introductory trio of topics in this *Things to Know* book by introducing learners to resources provided by private groups.

Preparation possibilities:

- Think about: Some private community resources your students may use or wish to use
- Bring to class: News stories about public or private community resources, especially any stories including debate about what resources should be private and which public

Technology resources:

- Search topics: *Charities, philanthropy*
- Web pages to try: National Charities Information Bureau, Canadian Non-Profit Resources Network

Student pages:

- Page 8 includes: An introduction to privately funded resources; a challenge story about a person finding local resources

- Page 9 includes: A word list you may adjust for your class, and student activities

Especially for ESL: Ask: Are most community resources private or public in your first country? Name some of each kind.

Extra idioms and slang to introduce:

- *You can't take it with you:* you can't use your money after you die (so you should use it now)
- *Take a look-see:* look around

Thoughts to share with learners: It isn't always easy to know whether community resources are private or public. Private groups, like hospitals, may use government money for some programs.

Questions to ask learners: What happens in bad economic times? Do we need more community resources, or fewer? Which resources do better in bad times—private ones, or public? Or does that depend on a lot of different things? Do you think the person in the story on page 8 does the right thing? Should the person take the reward? Why do people give money to community resources? Why don't they just keep it for themselves?

Projects to assign learners: Look around your town or city. Make a list of the community resources you might want to use. In the next week, visit three community resources you don't know much about.

A fascinating fact to share: In 1992, California had 17,885 nonprofit organizations. Most of them worked to help people, none to make money for themselves.

Lesson 3: Private Resources

Where do resources come from? Not just from governments. They can't do everything. Private groups help, too. A **nonprofit** store might sell used clothing. A church might help **homeless** people. A club might make a school playground. But lots of people use these things. So why do we call them private? Because of where they get their **funds**. Do **taxes** pay for something? Then it is public. Does the money come from somewhere else? Then it's private. Does this matter much? To the people who pay for the resources, yes. But people who use them may not care at all.

Challenge: Your new city

You live in a new city, and you love it. It looks nicer than the city you came from. That seemed unfriendly, and you didn't get out much. You spent most of your time at work or at home.

But you won't do that here. The new city feels like a better community. You want to find out all about it. So you decide to explore the area carefully, and write down all the community resources you might want to use.

The next morning you walk through a beautiful park. That's the first thing on your list. Then you add a library, a couple of schools, and a **hospital**. Next comes a **soup kitchen**. You hope you won't need that, but you never can tell.

You find a **museum**, too, and several **athletic fields**. What a wonderful city!

You wonder where all these community resources come from. Taxes pay for some, you are sure. But some seem to be private. Maybe there are some rich **philanthropists** around. They must make large **donations** to places like the museum. You wish you had that kind of

money. You would give some to **charities**. You would help make this city even better.

Then you look down at the sidewalk. There's a **wallet** that somebody lost. Maybe you are rich! You look inside and find more than $700. You also find the **identity** of the owner.

You call the owner when you get home, and she is very happy. "You have a **reward** coming," she says.

You think about that. You could use the money. But you

don't want to be paid for being honest. "No," you say. "I can't take it."

"Then I'll give $100 to your favorite **cause**," she says. "Just tell me where to send it."

Here's your challenge: What will you say? Where will the money go?

Life Skills Literacy:
Things to Know About Community Resources

Lesson 3: Private Resources

Word List

nonprofit	tax(es)	museum	donation(s)	identity
homeless	hospital	athletic field(s)	charities(y)	reward
fund(s)	soup kitchen	philanthropist(s)	wallet	cause

Increasing Your Understanding

1. Look at the word list in the box above. If you don't know a word, find out what it means. Try to figure it out from the way it is used on page 8. Or look it up in a dictionary.

2. Supply the missing word in each of the sentences below. Use the word list above.

   (a) In the story on page 8, you think there might be rich _____ around.

   (b) "I'll give $100 to your favorite _____," says the woman at the end of the story.

   (c) You would give some money to _____ if you could.

   (d) If _____ pay for something, it is public, says the paragraph at the top of page 8.

   (e) We call some resources private because of where they get their _____.

Questions to Discuss

1. How do you answer the challenge on page 8? What is your favorite cause?

2. What community resources are listed in the story on page 8? Which do you think are public? Which are private? (It may not be easy to tell.)

3. What kinds of community resources should taxes pay for? What kinds should private funds pay for? Brainstorm your answers. Talk about why you think the way you do.

Things to Write About

1. What is a community resource that you use? Is it private or public? Write a paragraph about it.

2. Write a letter asking for money. Choose a resource from the story on page 8. Write a letter asking people to give money to it. Say why donations are important. What will they be used for?

Things to Do

1. Act out the story on page 8 with a partner. Use your own names and words if you want. One of you can be the person in the story. The other can be a friend. Talk about what happens.

2. Make symbols to represent private and public community resources. Imagine that you have to make two lists. One is for private resources. The other is for public resources. Draw a symbol to put at the top of each list.

3. Decide on a new community resource for your area. Work with two or three classmates. Think of a new resource your town or city needs. What is it? Where will it be? Who will pay for it? Share your group's ideas with the class.

4. What kind of private resources are near you? Look around near your school and home. Share what you find with your class.

Life Skills Literacy:
Things to Know About Community Resources

Lesson 4: You and Community Resources

Themes:

- You as a user of resources
- Self-help in finding resources

Background notes: Community resources are available to everybody. In fact, the term "community" is sometimes used to mean "available to all"—as is the case, for example, with community theater. But access isn't everything, and some people don't make nearly as much use of community resources as they might. These pages introduce learners to the topics of access and use, and they give you the opportunity to encourage classes to make the greatest possible use of organizations and other resources available to them.

Preparation possibilities:

- <u>Think about</u>: Television and other broadcast resources in your area (See "Questions to ask learners" and "Projects to assign learners," below.)
- <u>Bring to class</u>: A listing of local community access TV channels; news stories about the accessibility of various local resources or any discrimination involved with them

Technology resources:

- Search topics: *Public access television, self-help*
- Web pages to try: Your Community On-Line Network (for local community information)

Student pages:

- Page 11 includes: A paragraph saying that everybody uses community resources of various types; a dialogue between two friends about taking advantage of resources

- Page 12 includes: A word list you may adjust for your class, and student activities

Especially for ESL: People new to their culture and community might need more help than others at identifying useful community resources. They might also be more hesitant than others to begin using those resources. Helping them know just where to go and how to find assistance may be very useful. Asking more experienced classmates to assist them may also be worthwhile.

Extra idioms and slang to introduce:

- *Have cold feet about something:* be nervous about something
- *Get around to something:* do something after a long wait

Thoughts to share with learners: You have the right to use many resources. Anti-discrimination laws cover many community resources. You can't be refused because of your skin color, your religion, your sex, or for other reasons like those.

Questions to ask learners: Who can use what resources? Think about some different kinds, and decide. (Can everybody use a city library? A road? An elementary school? A church? A soup kitchen? An outdoor club?) Are TV and radio stations good community resources in your town or city?

Projects to assign learners: Think about one TV program you like. List the community resources it shows. Share your ideas with the class. Try a new recreational resource in the next week.

A fascinating fact to share: An old law in Atlanta, Georgia, said that smelly people could not use streetcars.

Lesson 4: You and Community Resources

Who uses community resources? All of us do. We use some, like roads, almost every day. And some resources come to us. These **include** the **access channels** on TV. They **announce** local news. They say what will happen when. We have to look for other resources. But most aren't hard to find. People want you to know about them. Some are in the phone book. And some have ads in the paper. If you need something, look for it. Probably you'll find it. But there's one thing you won't find. You won't find people who don't need resources.

Dialogue: Who says you aren't rich?

First Friend: I'm so broke I can't even go to the movies. Why can't I be rich?

Second Friend: Maybe you already are. I think I'm rich. And I don't have much money either.

FF: Is this a **lecture**? Are you going to talk about all the good things in life?

SF: I'm going to talk about the good things in this community. It has all sorts of resources. That's why I feel rich. If I want to do something **cultural**, I can go to the art museum. That's free on Friday nights. And if I want outdoor **recreation** I can use the park.

FF: I suppose so, but you still need money.

SF: Of course. But not much. And think about this. School is free. That's a great resource, because getting an **education** can help you make money.

FF: School won't pay for **emergencies**.

SF: No, but the community helps. If you have a **medical** problem, go to a **clinic** or emergency room. If you have a fire, call for help.

FF: But I'm not sick. I just want something to do that doesn't cost a **fortune**.

SF: Then go to a church or a **social** club. This city must have 20 **organizations** you would like.

FF: Maybe. But I don't know what they are.

SF: That's because you never look. This city is full of resources, but it's up to you to find them. Take some **initiative**. You know what they say. Help goes to people who help themselves.

FF: I should have known what you'd say. I've heard your **self-help** lecture before.

SF: But you never listen. You just feel sorry for yourself. Hey! That's my wallet! What are you doing?

FF: I'm trying to find $10 for the movies. You said I should help myself.

SF: Hands off! That's not what I meant.

Life Skills Literacy:
Things to Know About Community Resources

Name_____ Date _____

Lesson 4: You and Community Resources

Word List

include	lecture	education	clinic	organization(s)
access channel(s)	cultural	emergencies(y)	fortune	initiative
announce	recreation	medical	social	self-help

Increasing Your Understanding

1. Look at the word list in the box above. If you don't know a word, find out what it means. Try to figure it out from the way it is used on page 11. Or look it up in a dictionary.

2. Supply the missing word in each of the sentences below. Use the word list above.

   (a) Resources that come to us _____ access channels, says the paragraph at the top of page 11.

   (b) One thing access channels do is _____ local news.

   (c) In the story on page 11, the first friend says school won't pay for _____.

   (d) "Is this a _____?" asks the first friend early in the story.

   (e) The first friend should take some _____, the second friend says.

Questions to Discuss

1. Is the second friend right in the story on page 11? Does help go to people who help themselves?

2. What kinds of resources does the story talk about? What other kinds can you think of? See how many you can brainstorm.

3. Can you be poor and rich at the same time? What does the second friend think? What do you think?

Things to Write About

1. What's a good recreation resource near you? Write a paragraph about it.

2. Can schools really help you earn money? How? Write your ideas.

Things to Do

1. Act out the story on page 11 with a partner. Use your own names and words if you want.

Talk about some social clubs in your area. Do you belong to any?

2. What resources come to people? Look at the paragraph on the top of page 11 again. List five different resources that come to people. Then list five that people have to go to.

3. Make your community sound like a good place to be. Imagine that you work for your town or city. You want it to grow. Work with two or three classmates. Write a radio ad telling people to move there. Talk about some resources the community offers. Share your ad with the whole class.

4. What's a great community resource in your area? Ask some friends and family members what they think. Share your answers with the class.

Lesson 5: You the Citizen

Themes:

- Citizen responsibilities
- Service to and through government

Background notes: Most of the lessons in this *Things to Know* book explore community resources that might be useful to learners. This lesson and the next, however, speak of ways that your students and others may be useful to the resources. Through these pages on government service, learners consider such subjects as voting, taxes, government jobs, and jury duty. But the pages only touch the surface of their subject matter. Learners who dig deeper will find a long list of government offices and programs that affect them and might use their help through either volunteer effort or employment.

Preparation possibilities:

- Think about: How much your learners are probably doing now for their governments in terms of taxes, voting, and employment
- Bring to class: Materials soliciting involvement in government activities, such as military recruiting pamphlets, get-out-the-vote materials

Technology resources:

- Search topics: *Government service, government jobs, voter registration, jury duty*
- Web pages to try: Voter registration (by town, city, state, or province)

Student pages:

- Page 14 includes: Ideas about contributing to government, with words from Lincoln's Gettysburg Address; a story about affecting city policy, with a quote from Kennedy's inaugural address

- Page 15 includes: A word list you may adjust for your class, and student activities

Especially for ESL: Many ESL students are not citizens, so cannot participate fully in some government activities. Ask: How can you support the governments where you live now? (See also Lesson 9.)

Extra idioms and slang to introduce:

- *Go the limit:* do as much as possible
- *Schmooze:* talk

Thoughts to share with learners: Some people who serve the government give a lot to do it—even if they get paid. In the military they might give their lives. And some government workers get a lot less pay from the government than they might get somewhere else. Some people who can use help from the government are the people who vote least often. They include poor people and young people.

Questions to ask learners: What if governments all cut taxes in half? How might that affect you? Does jury duty sound like fun to you? Have you ever done it? Do you know somebody who has? Why don't young people vote as often as they can?

Projects to assign learners: Find out how you can register to vote in your town or city. You might start by calling your city or town hall. Find out what your government wants from you. Look for posters, TV ads, and other things asking you to do something (like join the army). Share what you find with the class.

A fascinating fact to share: Until 1863, postal service in the United States was free.

Name_____ Date_____

Lesson 5: You the Citizen

In a **democracy**, government is not just *for* the people. It is also *by* the people. And it is *of* the people. President Lincoln said that. But what does it mean? It means that the government is ours. We can't just get things from it. We also must give things to it. That's what being a **citizen** is about. We have to **contribute** to the government. We contribute when we pay taxes, and when we give **service**. We contribute again when we give **allegiance** to the government. That means we support it most of the time. It doesn't mean that we agree with it all the time.

Story: A problem

Sun was angry. "We need a meeting right now," he told his roommates.

"What's going on?" asked Mara when all six were in the living room.

"You won't believe it," Sun told them. "The city wants to build a **parking garage** right here. They want to **demolish** this apartment house!"

"No!" shouted Annie.

"That's not right!" said Colin. "They can't do that!"

"Yes they can," said Sun.

Colin wasn't **convinced**. "How can they? Governments are supposed to help people, not hurt them."

"But some people think this is a good thing," Tom put in. "Parking garages are community resources. Everybody needs them."

"Not here they don't!" said Sun.

"Wait a minute," Lenya told them. "I remember what President Kennedy said. 'Ask not what your country can do for you,' he said. 'Ask what you can do for your country.'"

"What's that got to do with it?" asked Mara. "Anyway, this is just a city."

"Same idea," said Lenya. "And an **election** is coming right up. We can get people to vote for good **candidates** for the **city council**. Then they'll build their garage somewhere else. That's what we can do for our city."

The friends liked Lenya's idea. In the next week, they did some thinking and made a list of candidates to **support**.

"There's a problem," Annie told them. "We can tell other people who to vote for. But there isn't any good candidate in this **district**. Who will we vote for?"

"I think I know," said Tom. He pointed at Sun.

"What? Me? Run for city **councillor**?" said Sun. "I don't think so."

"Why not?" asked Annie. "You like **politics**."

"Yes, but being on the council is a whole lot of work."

"Just think about Kennedy and what he said," Lenya told him. "Maybe you'll be like him. The council today, the White House tomorrow."

Life Skills Literacy:
Things to Know About Community Resources

Name_____ Date _____

Lesson 5: You the Citizen

ACTIVITY PAGE

Word List

democracy	service	demolish	candidate(s)	district
citizen	allegiance	convince(d)	city council	councillor
contribute	parking garage	election	support	politics

Increasing Your Understanding

1. Look at the word list in the box above. If you don't know a word, find out what it means. Try to figure it out from the way it is used on page 14. Or look it up in a dictionary.

2. Supply the missing word(s) in each of the sentences below. Use the word list above.

   (a) We have to _____ to the government, says the paragraph at the top of page 14.

   (b) In a _____, government is not just *for* the people.

   (c) We contribute when we pay taxes and when we give _____ to the government.

   (d) Sun likes _____, says Annie in the story on page 14.

   (e) The city wants to _____ the friends' apartment house and make a _____.

Questions to Discuss

1. Should Sun run for city council in the story on page 14? Is that a good way to solve the friends' problem?

2. Do you agree with President Kennedy? Should everybody try to do something for their country? What are some ways people can serve their country? Can you serve your country and get paid for it? How? Brainstorm your answers.

3. Who should run for office? What kinds of people make good politicians and good leaders?

Things to Write About

1. How can you contribute to your city? Write a paragraph about your ideas.

2. Write a letter to your city council. Imagine that it wants to build a parking garage where people now live. Say that this is not a good idea, and give your reasons why.

Things to Do

1. Act out the story on page 14 with a partner. Take the parts of two friends in the story. Use your own names and words if you want. Talk about what the city wants to do and how you can stop it.

2. List at least seven jobs people can get with the government. Circle one or two that you might like to have.

3. Help get out the vote. Imagine that an election is coming, and you want to convince people to vote. Work with two or three other students and decide what you might do. Share your ideas with the class.

4. Who works for the government near you? Look around your home and school. How many government workers do you see? Share what you find with your class.

Life Skills Literacy:
Things to Know About Community Resources

Lesson 6: You the Volunteer

Themes:

- Helping to provide community resources
- Volunteering time and energy

Background notes: These pages point out the important role of volunteers in providing community resources, and lead learners to consider joining a cause. Extension activities offer a chance to explore volunteer efforts. You might consider focusing those activities on one or two local efforts requiring volunteer help, possibly efforts of particular concern to your school or students. In some school settings, full-class involvement in a volunteer effort might be appropriate.

Preparation possibilities:

- <u>Think about</u>: The volunteer needs of your community and the volunteer work your students do
- <u>Bring to class</u>: Materials about local volunteer programs and needs
- <u>Invite to class</u>: A representative of an agency providing volunteer services of interest to your class

Technology resources:

- Search topics: *Volunteers, volunteerism*
- Web pages to try: Points of Light Foundation (and specific organizations of interest by area)

Student pages:

- Page 17 includes: An introduction to the need for and rewards of volunteering, a challenge story about mandatory, school-based community service programs
- Page 18 includes: A word list you may adjust for your class, and student activities

Especially for ESL: ESL students who are new to this country may have received assistance from volunteer organizations that help immigrants and refugees. <u>Ask</u>: If you had such help, was it useful? Did the volunteers enjoy giving it? What can people volunteer for in your first country?

Extra idioms and slang to introduce:

- *Go the extra mile:* give a lot of effort
- *Put up or shut up:* do something or stop talking about it

Thoughts to share with learners: Most people who volunteer feel good about what they do. That's all the reward they want. But you can sometimes get more than that by volunteering. You might get good experience that will help you find a job, for example. Or you might make new friends.

Questions to ask learners: Who in the class does volunteer work? What is it? Where do most volunteers work? For public organizations? For private ones? Which kind needs volunteers more? How can organizations say "thank you" to their volunteers?

Projects to assign learners: Visit an organization you might want to volunteer in. Ask what jobs you might do. Decide if you want to volunteer there. What organizations near you want volunteers? Look on school bulletin boards or in the paper. Or watch community channels on TV. Share what you find with your class.

A fascinating fact to share: In 1996, Walter Annenberg said he would give all his artwork to a New York museum when he died. The art was then worth about $1 billion.

Lesson 6: You the Volunteer

"It takes a **village** to raise a child." Have you heard this before? It means that children need a lot of help. Adults do, too. So we set up groups to help each other. These are good resources. Still, they often need help, too. They don't run by themselves. They might have some **professional** workers. But they also need **volunteers**. Those are people who will make a **sacrifice**. They will give some time for other people. Why do they help? They like to. They feel good when they volunteer.

Challenge: The volunteer

Student: Did you want to see me?

Principal: Yes. Do you have a minute?

S: Sure.

P: I'm interested in your ideas about community service.

S: I think it's great for people who get helped. And it's great for people who volunteer.

P: I like your **attitude**. I think community service is important, too. In fact, I think this school should require students to do it.

S: You mean make a new rule? Saying that every student needs to earn community service **credits** by volunteering for so many hours?

P: Yes. And no student could **graduate** without that credit. Isn't that a great idea?

S: The whole city might **appreciate** student help.

P: There are lots of people with problems. And we need lots of agencies to help them. With a **mandatory** service program, we'd get lots of new volunteers.

S: Isn't there a problem here?

P: Not that I can see.

S: If students have to do something, they aren't really volunteers.

P: Oh, that's just playing with words. That's not a real **issue**. The important thing is the result. This program could build school **spirit**. And it could get our students new **recognition** in the community. What do you say?

S: I guess I have to think about all this.

P: Please do. And do your thinking tonight. I want you on a **committee** to help with the **program**. Your group will help set it up. You and some teachers and two more students will work together.

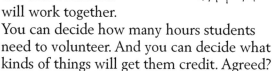

You can decide how many hours students need to volunteer. And you can decide what kinds of things will get them credit. Agreed?

S: I agree to think about it.

P: Okay. Come see me tomorrow. And remember, this committee will look good on your record.

> **Here's your challenge:** You be the student. What will you decide?

Life Skills Literacy:
Things to Know About Community Resources

Name_____ Date _____

Lesson 6: You the Volunteer

Word List

village	sacrifice	credit(s)	mandatory	recognition
professional	principal	graduate	issue	committee
volunteer(s)	attitude	appreciate	spirit	program

Increasing Your Understanding

1. Look at the word list in the box above. If you don't know a word, find out what it means. Try to figure it out from the way it is used on page 17. Or look it up in a dictionary.

2. Supply the missing word in each of the sentences below. Use the word list above.

   (a) The principal in the story on page 17 wants a _____ service program.

   (b) "I like your _____," the principal tells the student.

   (c) The student says the whole city might _____ student help.

   (d) "It takes a _____ to raise a child," according to the paragraph at the top of page 17.

   (e) Some community resources need both professional workers and _____.

Questions to Discuss

1. How do you answer the challenge on page 17? Does the principal make a good case?

2. Does the government care if people volunteer in private organizations? Why or why not? Should the government reward people who do? How could it do that?

3. Who saves lives? Look at the drawing at the top of page 17. What kind of organization might have a poster like that?

Things to Write About

1. What kind of volunteer work sounds good to you? Write a paragraph about it.

2. Has a volunteer ever helped you? Write about how you were helped.

Things to Do

1. Act out the story on page 17 with a partner. Use your own names and words if you want. Talk about what the principal means at the end of the story.

2. Do some math. Imagine that you work 5 hours a week for 50 weeks of every year. How long will it take you to work 1,000 hours?

3. Which organizations need professional workers? Which need volunteers? Which need both? Which need the most volunteers? Talk about these five organizations with two or three classmates: hospitals, schools, soup kitchens, the police, museums. Then see if other classmates agree with your ideas.

4. Who volunteers? Ask some friends and family members if they do. Share what you find with your class.

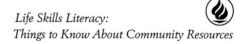

Lesson 7: Living Resources

Themes:

- Finding welfare assistance
- Connections between work and welfare

Background notes: The world of welfare sometimes seems to revolve around the phrase "it all depends." The nature and amount of benefits depend on essential questions about what, where, who, why, and when. Never was this more true in the United States than during the late 1990s, after passage of "welfare reform" shifted responsibility for many survival programs from the nation to its states. These pages present content and extension activities designed to help learners identify the resources available in their own areas. Students whose interest in the topic is high might appreciate visits from welfare workers or others with detailed knowledge of welfare programs in your area.

Preparation possibilities:

- <u>Think about</u>: How much interest your students are likely to have in welfare programs
- <u>Bring to class</u>: Names and addresses of welfare and related offices in your area

Technology resources:

- Search topics: *Welfare, food stamps, public housing, community organizations*
- Web pages to try: Welfare Information Network, The Child Welfare League of Canada

Student pages:

- Page 20 includes: An introduction to the idea of welfare; a dialogue about somebody getting off welfare

- Page 21 includes: A word list you may adjust for your class, and student activities

Especially for ESL: The U.S. Welfare Act of 1996 contained many anti-immigrant provisions, but 1998 legislation provided additional assistance of various types. Immigrants among your ESL students might benefit even more than others from knowing where they can learn about current local regulations.

Extra idioms and slang to introduce:

- *Turn the tables:* reverse things; change things around
- *Know-how:* skill and knowledge

Thoughts to share with learners: Community organizations in many cities help low-income people help themselves. A lot of them work on things like housing and welfare issues. In the United States there is no constitutional right to welfare. But some states say there is one.

Questions to ask learners: What does "poor" mean? (In 1996, the United States said a family of four was poor if it earned less than $15,600.) How can you help people with low incomes? (Work in soup kitchens, vote for leaders who will work for the poor, etc.)

Projects to assign learners: Find out where to learn about welfare and other benefits in your area. Visit a welfare office. Ask who is eligible for different benefits. Share what you find with your class.

A fascinating fact to share: In the 1994 U.S. national election, about 20 percent of people with less than $5,000 in income voted. More than 60 percent of people with income over $50,000 voted.

Lesson 7: Living Resources

READING PAGE

What if you're broke? And you can't find a job? Or you don't have a place to sleep? Where can you get help? That depends on where you live. Start with a phone book. Look up your town or city government. Look for the **welfare** office. Or see if you can find a **social services** number. Call either one and ask what to do. Or try the yellow pages. Look for a **heading** like "social and human services." Maybe you can find a **listing** for low-cost **legal** help, or a community organization near you. Call either one. Somebody will help you decide where to go next.

Dialogue: Welfare that worked

Welfare Worker: Hi. I didn't expect to see you back so soon. I thought we had your **benefits** all in order.

Recipient: We did. You helped me get cash **assistance** to build up my income. And you told me how to get food **stamps**.

WW: Then what can I do for you today?

R: I've got good news. I just found a great job. You can rip up all my paperwork. That's what I stopped by to tell you. I don't need a caseworker any more.

WW: That's wonderful. Where are you working?

R: At the new shopping mall just outside town.

WW: Do they pay pretty well?

R: Well enough so I won't be **eligible** for any more money. It's good-bye **poverty** and hello **paycheck** for me.

WW: So they pay well? Better than **minimum wage**?

R: A lot better. I can't **survive** on minimum wage. Not with three kids.

WW: I know. I couldn't either.

R: But why so interested? You've got a great job here.

WW: That's what I thought. But then that new mall came in. Everybody's getting great jobs. Everybody but me. The **unemployment** rate is going down so low they might not need me here. And I don't want to move to another welfare office.

R: How strange. You help me so I can get a new job. Then you might lose yours.

WW: I don't like it one bit.

R: Well, cheer up. You can get unemployment benefits for a while if you lose your job. And I can tell you which stores take food stamps.

WW: I already know, thanks. And stop smiling like that. This isn't funny.

R: Sorry. I'm not smiling at you. I'm just happy for me. And I know you'll do just fine. There's plenty of help around for people who need it.

Life Skills Literacy:
Things to Know About Community Resources

Name_____ Date _____

Lesson 7: Living Resources

Word List

welfare	listing	recipient	eligible	minimum wage
social service(s)	legal	assistance	poverty	survive
heading	benefit(s)	stamp(s)	paycheck	unemployment

Increasing Your Understanding

1. Look at the word list in the box above. If you don't know a word, find out what it means. Try to figure it out from the way it is used on page 20. Or look it up in a dictionary.

2. Supply the missing word(s) in each of the sentences below. Use the word list above.

   (a) If you need help, look for the _____ office, says the paragraph at the top of page 20.

   (b) You might also look for a _____ like "social and human services."

   (c) Maybe you will find a _____ for low-cost _____ help or a community organization.

   (d) In the story on page 20, the _____ rate is going way down.

   (e) "It's good-bye _____ and hello _____ for me," says the recipient.

Questions to Discuss

1. Who should run welfare programs? National governments? States and provinces? Cities and towns? What do you think?

2. What do most people need just to survive? Brainstorm your answers.

Things to Write About

1. How much should the government help? Imagine that somebody has no money and no job. What kind of help should the government give? Write your ideas in a paragraph.

2. Are food stamps a good way to help people? Should governments use them more than they do? Less than they do? Give your ideas in a letter to a government leader.

Things to Do

1. Act out the story on page 20 with a partner. Use your own names and words if you want.

Talk about unemployment in your area. Is it high or low?

2. What should food stamps buy? Think about the food stamps that some governments give people who need help. List five kinds of things food stamps should pay for. Then list five kinds of things they should not pay for.

3. Plan a new community organization. Work with two or three classmates. Imagine that you are setting up a new organization to help poor people help themselves. How will it work? What will it do? Brainstorm your answers. Then share the best ones with the whole class.

4. Is the recipient right in the story on page 20? Is there plenty of welfare and other help for people who need it? Ask friends and family members what they think. Share what you find with your class.

21   *Life Skills Literacy:*
Things to Know About Community Resources

Lesson 8: About Social Security

Themes:

- Social Security and its benefits
- Community resources and accident victims

Background notes: The New Deal of the 1930s marked a turning point in the history of American community resources. In the depths of the Great Depression, Franklin D. Roosevelt led the federal government in creating new programs and institutions to assist families and individuals in their struggle for economic survival. One of the most successful and popular was the Social Security Administration. These pages introduce learners to that organization and its benefits, then consider Social Security benefits as one among a number of resources available to the disabled.

Preparation possibilities:

- Think about: Whether your students are likely to need prompting to get Social Security numbers
- Bring to class: News stories about Social Security changes made or contemplated by Congress

Technology resources:

- Search topics: *Social Security Administration, retirement, disability benefits*
- Web pages to try: Social Security Education Center

Student pages:

- Page 23 includes: A Social Security Administration notice about getting information, an introduction to Social Security, and a story about resources helpful to a disabled accident victim
- Page 24 includes: A word list you may adjust for your class, and student activities

Especially for ESL: Legal immigrants are entitled to some Social Security benefits, and need numbers to get them. Ask: Does your first country have a program like Social Security?

Extra idioms and slang to introduce:

- *Golden years:* retirement
- *Over the hill:* old; past middle age

Thoughts to share with learners: Some people think the Social Security program is in trouble. One problem is that people live longer than they did when the program started in 1935. So it costs more to run than it did. If you think Social Security is important and should be saved, you should let your government leaders know.

Questions to ask learners: Who in the class has a job? Did you need a Social Security number to get it? Do you have a retirement plan in your job? When do people need to begin planning for retirement? What's the best time to call the toll-free number of the Social Security Administration? (See the box at the top of page 23.) Are Social Security benefits enough to live on? (Not very well.) How much will you need in retirement? (About 70 percent of your regular income, some experts say.)

Projects to assign learners: Find out where there's a Social Security office near you. Watch the news for stories about Social Security. When you find them, share them with your classmates.

A fascinating fact to share: In August of 1998, more than 44 million people received Social Security benefits. Of these, 5.5 million got them because of disabilities.

Name_____ Date_____

Lesson 8: About Social Security

 READING PAGE

Social Security Information

You can get more information 24 hours a day by calling **Social Security's toll-free** number, 800-772-1213. You can call for an **appointment** or to speak to a service **representative** between the hours of 7:00 A.M. and 7:00 p.m. on business days. Our lines are busiest early in the week and early in the month, so if your business can wait, it's best to call at other times. Whenever you call, have your Social Security number **handy**.

Americans need Social Security numbers. The law says so. You need them to work and use banks. You need them to use some government resources. You might get a number at birth. Or you can **apply** for it later. What will Social Security do for you? If you are **disabled**, it can pay you benefits. If you **retire**, you can get checks for the rest of your life. But you have to be at least 62 to do that. How can the government help so much? It takes money from people when they work. It gives the money back later on. In other words, it helps people save. Lots of people like this program.

Story: Her uncle's helper

Wanda got the call early in the morning. Her Uncle Abe was in the hospital. His card had hit a tree, and he might never walk again. Could Wanda come and help her Aunt Sarah?

Wanda phoned work and got **permission** to go away for a few days. She **packed** and took a bus to the airport.

When she landed in Los Angeles, a taxi brought her to the hospital. Her uncle was in pain and afraid. "I might be in a wheelchair all my life," he said. "What can I do? How can Sarah and I live?"

Wanda's aunt was frightened, too. "Will you help us?" she asked. "I don't know where else to turn."

"We'll find lots of help," Wanda said. The next day she talked to Jake, a hospital **social worker**.

"Of course I can help," he said. "One thing you can do is call the Social Security **Administration**. Some people think Social Security is just for retired people. But it has money for disabled people, too."

"My aunt and uncle are both very frightened," Wanda told him. "That may be their worst problem."

"I understand," said the social worker. "That's why the hospital has a **support group** for accident **victims**. They meet and talk about ways they can help themselves and each other."

"My uncle thinks he'll never work again."

"Not true," said Jake. "People with disabilities can get wonderful jobs. The local **vocational** school has a special training program for them."

"This all sounds good so far," said Wanda.

"Tell you what," said Jake. "You get some rest now. We'll meet for coffee tomorrow. I'll give you some ideas. And maybe I can show you around the city some."

"Sounds great," said Wanda. Maybe she would like Los Angeles. Maybe she would move here someday. Then she could really help her relatives.

SOCIAL SECURITY ADMINISTRATION

© 2001 J. Weston Walch, Publisher   23   *Life Skills Literacy:*
Things to Know About Community Resources

Lesson 8: About Social Security

ACTIVITY
PAGE

Word List

Social Security	representative	disabled	pack(ed)	support group
toll-free	handy	retire	social worker	victim(s)
appointment	apply	permission	administration	vocational

Increasing Your Understanding

1. Look at the word list in the box above. If you don't know a word, find out what it means. Try to figure it out from the way it is used on page 23. Or look it up in a dictionary.

2. Supply the missing word(s) in each of the sentences below. Use the word list above.

   (a) The box at the top of page 23 gives a _____ phone number you can use.

   (b) If you call, you can set up an _____ with the Social Security Administration.

   (c) You can get a Social Security number at birth or _____ for it later, says the paragraph at the top of page 23.

   (d) In the story on page 23, Wanda talks with a hospital _____ _____ named Jake.

   (e) Jake says the local _____ school has a training program for disabled people.

Questions to Discuss

1. What community resources does the story on page 23 talk about? What are some other resources that Wanda, her aunt, and her uncle might use?

2. Why do people need Social Security numbers? When do you have to use them?

3. Are social workers good community resources? Why do hospitals have them? What are some other things social workers do?

Things to Write About

1. Is Social Security a good idea? Or should everybody save their own money for when they retire? Write your ideas in a paragraph.

2. What kind of job training program might you want sometime? Where could you get it? Write your ideas.

Things to Do

1. With a partner, act out the parts of two people in the story on page 23. Use your own names and words if you want. Talk about where to get help if you have a bad accident.

2. Watch a television show about a community resource like a hospital. Tell your classmates about it.

3. Ask people to volunteer in hospitals. With two or three classmates, make up a radio ad for Your Town Hospital. Tell people how they can help. Then share your ad with the class.

4. Is it easy to get around public buildings near you in a wheelchair? Look around and find out. Talk about what you find with your classmates.

Lesson 9: Citizenship Services

TEACHER
PAGE

Themes:

- Immigration and naturalization services
- Special community resources for special people

Background notes: All community resources are not useful to all people. These pages make that point through information and extension activities as they introduce learners to immigration services and the naturalization process. Only through a pair of suggested questions does this material touch on the subject of resources for illegal newcomers to the United States. That topic is a hot one in some areas, and you may wish to consider making time for it in your own classes. If you find antagonism toward the idea of immigration among your students, you may also wish to mention that most American families were once new, and to discuss other diversity issues.

Preparation possibilities:

- Think about: Whether any of your students have a personal interest in citizenship services
- Bring to class: News stories about immigration events and policies   . .

Technology resources:

- Search topics: *Immigration, citizenship*
- Web pages to try: Immigration and Naturalization Service (INS), U.S. Citizenship Study Pages

Student pages:

- Page 26 includes: A phone listing for the INS; an introduction to the naturalization process; a challenge story about a citizenship interview

- Page 27 includes: A word list you may adjust for your class, and student activities

Especially for ESL: Newcomers to this country will of course have a special interest in this topic, and may also have good information and insights to share with other learners

Extra idioms and slang to introduce:

- *New kid on the block:* a newcomer
- *Nose around:* look for information

Thoughts to share with learners: The story on page 26 talks about an Alien Registration card. Some people call this a "green card" because that's the color used until 1996. Now the cards are pink. The story and the paragraph talk about a very common way to become a citizen. But there are other ways. For example, older people who have been in America for a long time may not need to take a test.

Questions to ask learners: Why do people move to America, or to other countries? (Immigrants usually come because they want to. Refugees often come because they are forced to leave their first countries.) Should the United States make community resources available to people who come illegally?

Projects to assign learners: Find out where there's an Immigration and Natural Services (INS) office near you. Find out about classes for immigrants. Do you have such community resources in your town or city? (Many schools offer both citizenship and English classes for newcomers.)

A fascinating fact to share: Twenty million people living in America in 1997 came from somewhere else. That's about 8 percent of the population.

25

Name_____ Date_____

Lesson 9: Citizenship Services

Phone Listing

UNITED STATES GOVERNMENT

JUSTICE DEPARTMENT
Immigration & Naturalization Service

Applications 123-4567
Ask Immigration
Toll-Free-Dial `1´ & Then...800-755-0777

Here's a phone book listing for part of the government. Who might use it? Anybody can, of course. But **aliens** might be more interested than other people. Aliens are people from other countries. They aren't U.S. citizens. But most of them can be if they want. How? The **process** has five steps. (1) You need to live here for a few years. (2) You need to apply. (3) You need to have an **interview**. (4) You need to take a test. (5) You need to take an oath. You can find out more by looking in the phone book for a listing like this, then calling the right number.

Challenge: The interview

Official: Please raise your right hand. Do you **solemnly swear** that you will tell the truth, the whole truth, and nothing but the truth?

Applicant: I do.

O: Thank you. Now sit down, and we can begin. Did you bring your identity cards?

A: Yes. Here's my Alien **Registration** card. And here's my Social Security card.

O: Has anything changed since you **submitted** your application?

A: No.

O: Good. Then I need to ask you some questions about government and history. When you answer, I'll find out how good your English is. You do need to understand English to pass.

A: I know. And I study English in school.

O: Here's your first question. Who was the first president of the United States?

A: George Washington.

O: That's right. What is **Congress**?

A: Do you smell something?

O: I'm sorry. That's wrong. Maybe if I speak slower, that will help. What is Congress?

A: I think I smell smoke.

O: No, that's not correct, either. But—what? You smell smoke? So do I!

A: Maybe there's a fire. Maybe we should leave. Maybe we should call 911.

O: I hear a siren. So somebody already called. Let's get out of here!

[Later, outside the building]

O: I'm glad it's only a wastebasket fire. We can **conclude** our interview in a few minutes. I see you know English. You have a good nose, too.

A: Will that make me a better citizen?

O: When there are fires, yes. Anyway, I think you'll probably pass. But while we wait, let me ask you one more thing. Why do you want to be a citizen?

> **Here's your challenge:** You be the applicant. Tell the official what citizenship means to you.

26

Life Skills Literacy:
Things to Know About Community Resources

Lesson 9: Citizenship Services

ACTIVITY PAGE

Word List

Justice Department	application(s)	interview	swear	submit(ted)
immigration	alien(s)	official	applicant	Congress
naturalization	process	solemnly	registration	conclude

Increasing Your Understanding

1. Look at the word list in the box above. If you don't know a word, find out what it means. Try to figure it out from the way it is used on page 26. Or look it up in a dictionary.

2. Supply the missing word(s) in each of the sentences below. Use the word list above.

   (a) The box at the top of page 26 shows numbers for the _____ & _____ Service.

   (b) To talk about _____, you call 123-4567.

   (c) "What is _____?" asks the official in the story on page 26.

   (d) The applicant has an Alien _____ card and a Social Security card.

   (e) _____ are people from other countries, according to the paragraph at the top of page 26.

Questions to Discuss

1. How do you answer the challenge on page 26? What does citizenship mean to you?

2. What kinds of community resources do new immigrants need? Which ones can volunteers work for?

3. Immigrants are a special group of people who need special help. What other groups need special community resources?

Things to Write About

1. What is it like to move to another country? Write a paragraph about that. If you have done this, say what you felt. If you haven't, guess what moving would be like.

2. How did your family come to your country? Tell the story in a sentence or two.

Things to Do

1. With a partner, act out the parts of the two people in the story on page 26. Use your own names and words if you want. Talk about how to do good interviews.

2. Make a drawing for the story on page 26.

3. What should aliens know before they become citizens? Work with two or three other students. List five things you think new citizens should know. Share your ideas with the whole class.

4. What special resources does your community have for special people? Look around and see. Share what you find with your class.

Lesson 10: State Schools

 **TEACHER PAGE**

Themes:

- Schools offered by different levels of government
- Schools and colleges as community resources

Background notes: U.S. census data show that in October of 1996, a full fourth of the population—70.3 million people—were enrolled in regular education programs, from nursery schools through colleges. But then, as now, schools had an impact far beyond the students enrolled in them and the teachers and other workers employed by them. They were community resources that offered building space for public use as well as student classrooms; musical, theatrical, and athletic entertainment as well as physical education training; and more, much more. These pages lead your learners to consider schools in their many useful roles.

Preparation possibilities:

- <u>Think about</u>: Your learners' experience and understanding of education at various levels
- <u>Bring to class</u>: News stories about educational resources in your area; catalogs and other materials pertaining to local and state or provincial schools

Technology resources:

- Search topics: *Education; educational statistics; schools, colleges, and universities*
- Web pages to try: National Center for Educational Statistics, schools and colleges by name

Student pages:

- Page 29 includes: An introduction to the schools run at different levels of government; a dialogue about funds schools

require and community resources they provide
- Page 30 includes: A word list you may adjust for your class, and student activities

Especially for ESL: Local schools are often among the first community resources experienced by refugees and immigrants to this country. But it may take some time for the newcomers to appreciate both the enormous size of their new country's educational establishment and the full range of services offered by schools. <u>Ask</u>: What services did schools provide in your first country?

Extra idioms and slang to introduce:

- *School of hard knocks:* experience
- *The old college try:* your best effort

Thoughts to share with learners: Schools are not all equal. Don't think that everything calling itself a school is good. Some are bad; they promise training they can't give, and they cheat students out of money. Ask around and be careful before you give any money to a school.

Questions to ask learners: What kinds of schools are the best community resources? *People get as much out of their public schools as they put into them.* What does this sentence mean? Do you agree?

Projects to assign learners: Find out how people who aren't students use your school. Visit a college or university in your area. Does it look like a good place to attend? Share what you find with your classmates.

A fascinating fact to share: Public education in the U.S. costs more than half a trillion dollars every year. That's more than $500,000,000,000.00.

Name_____ Date_____

Lesson 10: State Schools

Who needs schools? Kids might ask that question. But older people know the answer. Everybody needs schools. That's why we have so many. Even small towns have **elementary** schools. Most have middle schools and high schools, too. And all states have **colleges** or **universities**. There are also some **national** schools. Our schools are very different. No two are the same. But they all have one thing in common. They are all good community resources. That's why everybody needs them.

Dialogue: Paying for schools

School Opponent: Hi, are you a local voter?

Taxpayer: Yes, I am.

SO: Can I talk to you about next week's **referendum**?

T: The **bond issue**?

SO: Yes, the one that asks us to fund new buildings at the state university.

T: I think it's a great idea. I'm voting "Yes."

SO: I'm sorry to hear that. I think it's a waste of money. My group doesn't think taxpayers should have to pay for a university. Why spend all that money on a few lucky rich kids?

T: It isn't just for rich kids. It has a great **scholarship** program. And lots of students work their way through.

SO: Are you a student there?

T: Not right now. But I might take some courses next year.

SO: Then maybe I should **campaign** somewhere else.

T: Don't go away. Let's talk. I think you don't understand something. Our state university helps a lot of people who aren't students.

SO: Sure. The people who work there.

T: Not just them. The school does **research**. That helps businesses and farmers and all of us. And it has great football games and musical **entertainment**. Anybody can go to those things. And anybody can take night classes and work toward a **degree**.

SO: Everybody doesn't need a degree.

T: No, but everybody needs some education.

SO: I don't have a degree. And I'm a very **successful** businessperson. When people hear my name, they know who I am. I've earned a lot of money with my business.

T: Good for you. Then I've got an idea for you.

SO: What?

T: Give some to the school for a building. Then taxpayers won't need to buy it. Everybody wins.

SO: Everybody but me!

T: Don't be so sure. I bet they'll name the building after you.

SO: Really? Are you serious?

© 2001 J. Weston Walch, Publisher   29   *Life Skills Literacy: Things to Know About Community Resources*

Name_____ Date _____

Lesson 10: State Schools

ACTIVITY PAGE

Word List

elementary	national	bond issue	research	successful
college(s)	opponent	scholarship	entertainment	
universities(y)	referendum	campaign	degree	

Increasing Your Understanding

1. Look at the word list in the box above. If you don't know a word, find out what it means. Try to figure it out from the way it is used on page 29. Or look it up in a dictionary.

2. Supply the missing word(s) in each of the sentences below. Use the word list above.

   (a) The opponent in the story on page 29 wants to talk about next week's _____.

   (b) "Maybe I should _____ somewhere else," says the opponent.

   (c) The university has great football games and musical _____, according to the taxpayer.

   (d) All states have _____ or _____, says the paragraph at the top of page 29.

   (e) Even small towns have _____ schools.

Questions to Discuss

1. Who is right in the story on page 29? Is the bond issue a good idea?

2. Why do we have both public and private schools? Should the government give money to private schools? Why or why not?

3. What kinds of schools are there? See how many the class can think of in two minutes. Then decide who runs each school on your list.

Things to Write About

1. Are state colleges good community resources? Write your ideas in a paragraph.

2. Write a short radio ad for the story on page 29. Tell people why they should vote for or against the referendum. Imagine that the school will use the money to build classrooms.

Things to Do

1. With a partner, act out the story on page 29. Use your own names and words if you want. Add some of your own ideas to the talk.

2. What do high schools do for their towns and cities? List at least seven things.

3. What does your school need? Work with two or three classmates. Decide on something the school needs. Then plan a campaign to get money for it. Who might make a donation? How can you convince them to do it? Share your ideas with your class.

4. Does your town or city have all the schools it needs? Look around and see what you think. Share your ideas with your classmates.

Life Skills Literacy:
Things to Know About Community Resources

Lesson 11: Courts and More

Themes:
- Types of courts
- Small claims courts

Background notes: "For many persons, law appears to be magic—an obscure domain that can be fathomed only by the professional initiated into its mysteries." So states *The Rights of the Poor*, a handbook published by the American Civil Liberties Union in 1997. One way to demystify the law is to approach the subject through one small piece, then build on the understanding that results. That's the tactic of these pages. They introduce learners to the legal system through small claims courts plus a quick glimpse at the whole system, then offer extension activities to provide a wider view.

Preparation possibilities:
- Think about: The part of the legal system of probable greatest interest to your learners
- Bring to class: Information about local courts and other parts of the legal system

Technology resources:
- Search topics: *Legal system, small claims courts*
- Web pages to try: California Small Claims Internet Information Center, New York Small Claims Guide

Student pages:
- Page 32 includes: A paragraph of text from a form used by small claims courts of California; a brief introduction to the legal system; a story about using a small claims court. Note that the form includes text at a higher reading level than most material in this *Things to Know* book.
- Page 33 includes: A word list you may adjust for your class, and student activities

Especially for ESL: Because the language of the legal system is so specialized, ESL students may find courts and related topics more difficult to understand than other aspects of their new culture. Ask: Do any legal offices offer assistance in your first language?

Extra idioms and slang to introduce:
- *Open-and-shut case:* an easy legal case
- *No-brainer:* an easy question

Thoughts to share with learners: The legal system includes a lot more than courts. Small claims courts are quite easy to understand. Some other courts are not. They are good community resources, but people shouldn't use them without the help of lawyers. Many large communities have legal aid resources to help people who can't afford to pay lawyers. In some places, small claims are settled by mediators, not judges.

Questions to ask learners: What are some other pieces of the legal system? What are some good jobs in the legal system? What do you think of the legal system? Is it good? Does it do its job well?

Projects to assign learners: Find out where there's a small claims or traffic court. Visit a court and watch a trial. Or watch a real trial on television. Share what you find with your classmates.

A fascinating fact to share: "Red tape" refers to government forms and processes that take a lot of time. The name came centuries ago from the color of the tape used to tie up official papers in England.

Lesson 11: Courts and More

▷ *[handwritten foreign script]*

[handwritten foreign script]

[handwritten foreign script]

▷ Information for Defendant

What is the **small claims court?** The small claims court is a special court in which **disagreements** are **resolved** quickly and cheaply. A small claim must be for $5,000 or less. The party who **sues** is called the **plaintiff**. The party who is sued is called the **defendant**. Neither party can be **represented** by a **lawyer** at the **trial** but either party may talk to a lawyer about the case.

We talk about "the legal system." But it's really a lot of different systems. There are **federal** courts and state courts. There are city courts and **county** courts. There are family courts and traffic courts. There are **criminal** courts and **civil** courts. Do you need to use a court? Then first you need to think about your problem. Does somebody owe you $1,000? Then maybe small claims court is for you. Is there trouble with somebody's will? Then you need a **probate** court.

Story: "It's in the mail."

"A thousand dollars is a lot of money," said Andrea. "I've got to get it back."

"I know," said John. "We need it to pay the rent. Mrs. Saih isn't being fair. I thought she would do better than that."

"Me too. She wasn't just my boss. She was also my friend. She still would be, if we didn't have this problem."

"Have you called her?"

"Three times. And every time she says the same thing. She says she sent the check. She says it's in the mail."

"That's what people always say. 'It's in the mail.' But it isn't. I think it's time to sue."

The next day Andrea went to small claims court. She picked up a form and brought it home to study. She learned that the process was easy. She needed to fill out the form and turn it into the court. Next she had to get a copy to Mrs. Saih. Then there would be a trial.

In court, Andrea would tell the judge what happened. She would say that Mrs. Saih owed her $1,000 when she left her job. Mrs. Saih

promised to pay, but never did. Mrs. Saih could also tell the judge her side of the story. Then the judge would make a decision. Andrea thought the judge would make Mrs. Saih pay. Even Mrs. Saih said that Andrea had the money coming.

So Andrea filled the form out and took it back to court. She **arranged** to have a copy sent to Mrs. Saih the next day. Then she went home and told John her news.

"Oh no!" said John. "That's terrible. You can't sue her."

"Of course I can," said Andrea. "You told me to."

"But her check is here. I found it with some other letters behind the bookcase!"

"Now what do I do?" asked Andrea.

Life Skills Literacy: Things to Know About Community Resources

Lesson 11: Courts and More

ACTIVITY
PAGE

Word List

small claims court	sue(s)	represent(ed)	federal	civil
disagreement(s)	plaintiff	lawyer	county	probate
resolve(d)	defendant	trial	criminal	arrange(d)

Increasing Your Understanding

1. Look at the word list in the box above. If you don't know a word, find out what it means. Try to figure it out from the way it is used on page 32. Or look it up in a dictionary.

2. Supply the missing word(s) in each of the sentences below. Use the word list above.

   (a) The form at the top of page 32 talks about _____.

   (b) The _____ is the person being sued.

   (c) Neither party can be _____ by a _____ at the trial.

   (d) "There are _____ and civil courts," according to the paragraph at the top of page 32.

   (e) In the story on page 32, Andrea _____ to have a copy of a form sent to Mrs. Saih.

Questions to Discuss

1. Does Andrea go to court too soon in the story on page 32? What else could she have done?

2. Are small claims courts a good idea? What might happen if a state didn't have them?

3. What can people do instead of suing each other? What are some good ways to solve problems like the one in the story on page 32?

Things to Write About

1. Would you like to be a judge? Give your answer in a paragraph.

2. Get your money back. Imagine that you are Andrea in the story on page 32. Write Mrs. Saih a letter asking for your $1,000. Tell her what you might do if you don't get it.

Things to Do

1. With a partner, act out the story on page 32. Use your own names and words if you want. Decide what Andrea should do next.

2. What kind of person makes a good lawyer? List at least five of your ideas. Start with "honest" if you want to.

3. Role-play a small claims trial. Work with three or more other students and decide on a case. Use the one in the story on page 32 if you want. Then have a trial. Share the results with the rest of your class.

4. What courts can you find near you? Look around your area and tell your class what you find.

Lesson 12: Job Resources

Themes:

- Employment resources
- Unemployment benefits

Background notes: Employment-related community resources today are an interesting mix, often provided by businesses and the federal government through a large variety of state and local agencies. Some, like basic unemployment benefits, are intended for temporary worker protection. Others, like the school-to-work programs of recent years, are partly a response to rapid technological change and intended for long-term worker training and development. These pages introduce learners to the basic benefits and offer extension activities inviting exploration of other resources.

Preparation possibilities:

- <u>Think about</u>: Local employment resources of possible interest to your students
- <u>Bring to class</u>: Information about local employment agencies and resources, and about any school-to-work programs available in your own school or community
- <u>Invite to class</u>: The representative of a local employment or work training agency

Technology resources:

- Search topics: *Unemployment benefits, job training*
- Web pages to try: Department of Labor Office of Employment and Training Administration, School-to-Work, Unemployment Insurance Institute

Student pages:

- Page 35 includes: An introduction to unemployment benefits; a challenge story

about a worker considering the long-term benefits of a high school diploma
- Page 36 includes: A word list you may adjust for your class, and student activities

Especially for ESL: <u>Ask</u>: What kinds of employment resources can you find in your first country? Do people get government help if they are out of work?

Extra idioms and slang to introduce:

- *Get the ax:* be fired
- *Talk turkey:* speak frankly

Thoughts to share with learners: Employers help pay the unemployment benefits of people who lose their jobs. In 1998, Congress passed a "Workforce Investment Act." It will give $5 billion in federal money to states and cities for job programs.

Questions to ask learners: How is the economy right now? Are jobs easy to get? Hard? Which is more important for most people? Getting good training? Or earning a lot right now? What if you don't know what kind of work you want to do? How can you decide? What kinds of resources can help you? What should the government do? Spend a lot of money on welfare? Or spend more money on job training programs?

Projects to assign learners: Look at the phone book and some local newspapers. Decide who can help people find jobs.

A fascinating fact to share: Around 1900, about one quarter of American boys aged 10 to 15 had jobs.

Lesson 12: Job Resources

Avoiding Problems with Claims

You can avoid most problems with Unemployment **Compensation** Claims. Just do these six things:

File claims as **instructed.**

Report all your work and **earnings.**

Answer questions completely and **accurately.**

Look for work.

Keep a list of your job **contacts** on the right form.

Ask questions when you do not understand what to do.

Have you lost your job? Maybe your state can help you. Did your company close? Or did it lay off lots of workers? Then the job loss wasn't your fault. Maybe you can get cash benefits. Ask at an office like the one in the picture. Even if you quit your job, you could get help. States and cities have many employment resources. Some offer training for jobs, and others list job openings. Governments want people to work. That helps everybody. But high unemployment hurts people. It causes more problems than you can count.

Challenge: The next job

Job Counselor: I understand you lost your job when the Acme **factory** closed.

Worker: That's correct. Now I'm applying for unemployment compensation.

JC: You had your job for two years, so I'm sure you **qualify.** But I don't think you'll need the benefits for long.

W: Why not?

JC: Because the **economy** is so good right now. There are lots of jobs around. Some pay much better than the factory did.

W: That's what I wanted to hear. "Get to the top of the pay heap." That's my **motto.**

JC: I understand your attitude. But let me suggest something else. Maybe you should take a lower-paying job.

W: Are you crazy?

JC: Excuse me?

W: I'm sorry. I shouldn't have said that. I didn't mean it. But why should I take lower pay?

JC: Because it has more **potential.** There's a real chance for **advancement** with the job I have in mind.

W: Maybe you are right.

JC: And maybe you should think about something else. I see from your form that you are not a high school graduate.

W: But I still keep finding work.

JC: I know. But believe me, a diploma will count in the long run. Your chances of **promotion** will go up if you get it.

W: I guess so. But I need more money right now. Besides, classes take a lot of time. Time when I can't work or have fun.

JC: Yes. But I know of one good job very close to a night school. You can work all day, take some classes, and still have time for yourself.

W: That sounds hard to me.

JC: It might be. But at least think about it.

Here's your challenge: Imagine that you are the worker. What will you do?

Life Skills Literacy:
Things to Know About Community Resources

Name_____ Date _____

Lesson 12: Job Resources

Word List

avoid(ing)	instruct(ed)	contact(s)	qualify	potential
claim(s)	earnings	counselor	economy	advancement
compensation	accurately	factory	motto	promotion

Increasing Your Understanding

1. Look at the word list in the box above. If you don't know a word, find out what it means. Try to figure it out from the way it is used on page 35. Or look it up in a dictionary.

2. Supply the missing word in each of the sentences below. Use the word list above.

   (a) In the story on page 35, the job counselor says the _____ is good right now.

   (b) There's a real chance for _____ in one job the counselor has in mind.

   (c) "Get to the top of the pay heap" is the worker's _____.

   (d) "Keep a list of your job _____," says the sign in the drawing on page 35

   (e) People should answer questions completely and _____, the sign says.

Questions to Discuss

1. How do you answer the challenge on page 35? Is the counselor right? Can a diploma help somebody earn more?

2. Why do states pay unemployment benefits? Why do they pay only when a job loss is not the worker's fault? Should they also pay when workers quit their jobs?

3. In the story on page 35, the counselor says that the economy is good. What does that mean? What is a bad economy like? What resources do people need in a bad economy?

Things to Write About

1. Why do employers care if workers have diplomas? Write a paragraph giving your answer.

2. Are you a good worker? Write two or three reasons why somebody should hire you.

Things to Do

1. Act out the story on page 35 with a partner. Use your own names and words if you want. Talk about how it feels to lose a job.

2. Do the math. Imagine that you can earn 2 dollars more an hour if you have a high school diploma. How much more can you earn in a 40-hour week? In a year? In 30 years?

3. Work with two or three classmates, and make a sign telling students to stay in school. Think up a good motto to put on it. Share your sign with the whole class.

4. What employment resources can you find near you? Look around. Then tell your class what you find.

Lesson 13: Emergency Resources

Themes:

- Emergency resources
- Volunteer emergency workers

Background notes: Emergency resources are numerous in the United States and Canada. They need to be. In the United States alone, two million fires are reported each year. And the United States suffers one of the highest fire death rates in the industrialized world, with 80 percent of the deaths occurring in home fires. These pages introduce learners to emergency resources in general, and give special attention to volunteer fire departments. Discussion and other extension activities lead students to consider the resources and needs of their own communities.

Preparation possibilities:

- Think about: The need for volunteer emergency workers in your community
- Bring to class: Information about fire prevention and volunteering for local emergency services

Technology resources:

- Search topics: *Fire protection, fire departments, volunteer fire departments*
- Web pages to try: International Association of Firefighters, Fire Department Training Network, U.S. Fire Administration

Student pages:

- Page 38 includes: An introduction to general emergency services; a dialog about recruitment for a volunteer fire department
- Page 39 includes: A word list you may adjust for your class, and student activities

Especially for ESL: Ask: What kinds of emergency resources does your first country have? Does it use volunteer firefighters, or professionals?

Extra idioms and slang to introduce:

- *Like a house on fire:* fast and strong
- *Burned, burned up:* very angry

Thoughts to share with learners: Emergencies are everybody's business. Professional firefighters and others can deal with most of them. But all of us can work at preventing some types of emergencies and helping each other when trouble strikes. The 911 emergency number is not yet available everywhere. Some people need to remember different emergency numbers in their communities.

Questions to ask learners: Who in the class does volunteer emergency work? Who wants to be an emergency worker? What kind of person makes a good emergency worker? Does your town or city have all the emergency resources it needs?

Projects to assign learners: Visit an emergency resource in your area. Find out what it does, and ask if it uses volunteers. Look for news stories about emergencies. What resources are used? Share what you find with your classmates.

A fascinating fact to share: In 24 B.C., the Emperor Augustus appointed the first firefighters in ancient Rome. Then, and for centuries after, the best fire-fighting tools were buckets filled with water.

Name_____ Date_____

Lesson 13: Emergency Resources

READING PAGE

Who helps in emergencies? Governments do. In big **disasters**, like **floods**, help comes from the national level. In forest fires, states do a lot. Towns and cities take care of smaller problems. They use **police** and fire departments for that. Private groups also help. The Red Cross may be the best known group. It helps many people in trouble. The rest of us can help, too. Most of us try to help when we see problems. But many people do more. Some volunteer to fight fires. Some work with the police. Why? They care about people. They like **excitement**, too.

Dialogue: The fire department

Firefighter: You're new in town, aren't you?

Newcomer: Yes, I am.

FF: I'm in the volunteer fire department. Can I interest you in **joining**?

N: I don't think that's for me.

FF: But we need people. You can save people's lives. And you get to drive a fire truck. Imagine racing down the road with the **sirens** in your ear. That's exciting.

N: I'm sure it is. But it might be too much for me.

FF: It doesn't happen very often, of course. But when it does, it's like WOW!

N: What kind of **commitment** is it?

FF: We have training once a month. Sometimes it's indoors, in a class. And sometimes we burn down buildings to **practice** on them.

N: That would be a problem for me. You see . . .

FF: But it's fun. And the other thing we do is educate people in the community. We tell them how to **prevent** fires. And we teach them about calling for emergency help.

N: Isn't that pretty simple? Don't you just dial 911?

FF: Yes, if you have a real emergency. But some people don't understand that. They call for the wrong reasons. They call because their cat is up a tree. Or they call to talk to a member of the department. Or they call to ask where the fire is when they hear a siren. That's really bad. So we need to teach people what to do.

N: Preventing fires and putting them out are very important. I think your department does wonderful work.

FF: Thank you. So do I. Now, will you join us?

N: I'm afraid I can't.

FF: Can't or won't?

N: Can't. That's what I've been trying to tell you. I'm **allergic** to smoke. It makes me sick. You don't want me anywhere near a fire.

Life Skills Literacy:
Things to Know About Community Resources

Name_____ Date _____

Lesson 13: Emergency Resources

Word List

department	junior	flood(s)	join(ing)	practice
membership	regular	police	siren(s)	prevent
cadet	disaster(s)	excitement	commitment	allergic

Increasing Your Understanding

1. Look at the word list in the box above. If you don't know a word, find out what it means. Try to figure it out from the way it is used on page 38. Or look it up in a dictionary.

2. Supply the missing word in each of the sentences below. Use the word list above.

   (a) The sign on page 38 says _____ members are aged 14 to 16.

   (b) Adult volunteers are called _____ members.

   (c) Some volunteers like _____, according to the paragraph at the top of page 38.

   (d) In big _____ like floods, help comes from the national level.

   (e) In the story on page 38, the newcomer is _____ to smoke.

Questions to Discuss

1. Do you think the firefighter in the story on page 38 is a good one?
2. What might cadets do in a volunteer fire department? What about junior members?
3. What can happen if somebody calls 911 when there's no emergency?

Things to Write About

1. What emergencies have you seen? Write a paragraph about one of them.
2. Imagine that you have a small fire in your house. The fire department puts it out. Write a letter saying thank you. Make up any facts you want to.

Things to Do

1. With a partner, act out the story on page 38. Use your own names and words if you want. Talk about how it might feel to fight fires.
2. When should you call 911? List five things that might make you call.
3. How can you prevent house fires? Work with two or three classmates. Create a television ad showing people something they should do. Act out your ad for the class.
4. What emergency resources are near you? Look around and tell your class what you find.

Lesson 14: City Hall Resources

Themes:

- Local government resources
- City and town halls

Background notes: City and town halls are mysterious places to some people. They seldom or never visit—or if they do, they go straight to a single department, do their business, and leave. These pages introduce learners to the idea of city hall as something useful to them, and, through extension activities, suggest a visit and tour. They assume the presence of a city or town hall in students' communities. If that is not the case for your classes, you might consider making adjustments in your presentation. In any event, you might consider arranging a class tour of a local government facility. But note that some city halls are more accessible than others; check yours before making plans. (See also Number 4 under "Things to Do" on page 42.)

Preparation possibilities:

- <u>Think about</u>: The structure of your own local government
- <u>Bring to class</u>: Information about local government structure and resources

Technology resources:

- Search topics: *City government, town government, local government, term limits*
- Web pages to try: National City Government Resource Center, Official City Site

Student pages:

- Page 41 includes: An introduction to local governments; a story about a candidate running for mayor
- Page 42 includes: A word list you may adjust for your class, and student activities

Especially for ESL: <u>Ask</u>: How do local governments operate in your first country? Do they have city or town halls?

Extra idioms and slang to introduce:

- *Dirty pool:* an unfair act
- *Bum steer:* bad information

Thoughts to share with learners: Some people are nervous about going to government offices. They shouldn't be. Government offices really are supposed to help people. Many people think it's not good for one person to stay in the same elected office for a long time. That's why some states and towns have term limits. U.S. presidents have term limits, too. They can only serve two full terms.

Questions to ask learners: Who in the class has used city hall? Do you want to tell the story? Was your experience good? Were the workers at city hall helpful? How can your own local government be better? Does it have a town or city council? A mayor? If not, what is the government like?

Projects to assign learners: Ask some friends and family members what they think of your local government. Share what you learn with your class. List some of the buildings run by your city or town government. Then list some local buildings run by other levels of government, like the state or county.

A fascinating fact to share: Reykjavik is the capital of Iceland. It has some unusual resources—underground hot springs that heat the entire city.

Lesson 14: City Hall Resources

"You can't fight city hall." That's a **common** saying. But usually you don't have to fight city hall. It's the center of **local** government. It has resources for everybody, and it should work for everybody. You can use city hall, instead of fighting it. But to use resources, people need to know about them. They can find out about their own city hall in the phone book. Or they can visit it. That's usually their right. City hall is like other parts of the government. It belongs to the people.

Story: The candidate

Sue Ann Lu was walking when a man asked for a minute of her time. "Are you registered to **vote** in this city?" he asked.

Sue Ann said she was.

"I'm Dan Schwartz," he said. "I'm a candidate for **mayor**."

"I've seen your picture in the news," she told him.

"I hope you think I'm good news. I will be if I win, because I want to **reform** our city government."

"So I hear," said Sue Ann. "May I ask why?"

"In the first place," Dan said, "city hall should be **accessible** to everybody."

"Can't everybody use it now?"

"Not easily. The health clinic isn't even open in the evenings. And that's when people need it."

Sue Ann knew the clinic was open two nights a week, and told him so.

"I'll have to check," said Dan. "Another thing is police **brutality**. Every day the news talks about another case."

"Really? The last one I remember was two months ago."

"Well, I'll have to **admit** that this is an unusually quiet **period**. But that won't continue if we leave this city in the hands of **politicians**."

"But aren't you a politician?"

"In a way. But not a **career** politician like my opponent. She's the **incumbent**, you know, and she's been in office a long time. When people stay in office too long, that's when **corruption** begins."

"Are you saying your opponent is corrupt?" Sue Ann wasn't looking happy.

"I hate to ask, but who knows where she gets all that money she spends on ads?"

"There was a story about that in last week's paper."

"You're very well **informed**, aren't you?" asked the candidate. "I could use somebody like you to help in my campaign. Interested?"

"Not a chance," said Sue Ann. "Your opponent happens to be my mother. And I happen to know she's not corrupt."

Life Skills Literacy:
Things to Know About Community Resources

Lesson 14: City Hall Resources

ACTIVITY
PAGE

Word List

common	mayor	brutality	politician(s)	corruption
local	reform	admit	career	inform(ed)
vote	accessible	period	incumbent	

Increasing Your Understanding

1. Look at the word list in the box above. If you don't know a word, find out what it means. Try to figure it out from the way it is used on page 41. Or look it up in a dictionary.

2. Supply the missing word in each of the sentences below. Use the word list above.

   (a) In the story on page 41, Dan Schwartz says Sue Ann Lu is very well _____.

   (b) "I want to _____ our city government," the candidate says.

   (c) He thinks there is a problem with police _____ in the city.

   (d) City hall is the center of _____ government, says the paragraph at the top of page 41.

   (e) According to a _____ saying, "You can't fight city hall."

Questions to Discuss

1. What do you think of the candidate in the story on page 41? Would you vote for him?

2. What does it mean to say you can't fight city hall? Why do people say that?

3. How do you feel about career politicians? Are they good for government, or not?

Things to Write About

1. What would you do if you were a mayor? Imagine that you have been elected in your town or city. How can you help your community? Write your ideas in a paragraph.

2. Write a letter to a mayor. Use any name you want. Tell the mayor why public health clinics need to be open at night.

Things to Do

1. Act out the story on page 41 with a partner. Use your own names and words if you want. Decide what you think will happen next.

2. What resources do most town and city governments offer? List at least seven things. Share them with your classmates.

3. How can you get elected to your town government? Imagine that you are helping a friend campaign. What will you do? Work with two or three other students and decide. Share your ideas with the class.

4. Visit your town or city hall. See what resources it offers. Share what you find with your class.

Lesson 15: Information Resources

TEACHER PAGE

Themes:

- The information age
- Library resources

Background notes: Information resources abound. Even the labels on food containers convey useful facts. But the random acquisition of facts is not sufficient for those who would prosper in contemporary society. A more purposeful approach is required. These pages introduce learners to some of the richest sources of information available today, libraries and the Internet. Extension activities lead them to consider some other resources. If your classes seem unfamiliar with useful local resources like libraries, you might consider organizing an exploratory class visit.

Preparation possibilities:

- Think about: Local information resources, including school and public libraries
- Bring to class: Examples of useful information resources, including such things as newspapers
- Invite to class: A teacher or librarian who can introduce students to the Internet and other electronic resources

Technology resources:

- Search topics: *Libraries, information age, research* (and libraries by name)
- Web pages to try: U.S. Public Libraries with Internet Services, Digital Library Resources

Student pages:

- Page 44 includes: An introduction to the information age and various resources; a

challenge story about what information resources a library should provide
- Page 45 includes: A word list you may adjust for your class, and student activities

Especially for ESL: <u>Ask</u>: What kinds of information resources did you use in your first country? What kinds do you use here? What kinds are most important for newcomers to this country?

Extra idioms and slang to introduce:

- *Snail mail:* regular mail (not e-mail)
- *Book it:* go quickly

Thoughts to share with learners: In the past, many people worked at the same job for most of their working lives. Now more and more people change careers several times. Every time they do, they need new information and information resources to help them.

Questions to ask learners: What kind of information resources can you find in a kitchen? A drugstore? A car? Who in the class uses computers? Where? Who uses e-mail? Who uses the Internet? How do you like electronic resources?

Projects to assign learners: Visit one local library and make a list of its resources. Sign up for a library card if you don't have one already. Try out a computer if you can. Ask some friends and family members how often they use computers. What for? Do they like them?

A fascinating fact to share: The U.S. Library of Congress in Washington, DC, has more than 100 million items. In 1997, it had 532 miles of book shelves, and more than 4,600 employees.

Name_____ Date_____

Lesson 15: Information Resources

Some parts of **history** have names. Long ago there were stone ages and an ice age. But what about now? This is "the **information** age," some people say. Why? Because information is such a big thing. More and more people get paid to work with it. Some are **librarians**. Some work in schools, and some make books. And some work with the **Internet**. They all share one thing. They work with **knowledge**. They help people learn things in many different ways. That's good, because the world is changing very fast. We all need to know new information all the time.

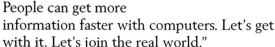

Challenge: The **decision**

You work for a library in a small city. Not long ago, it got a gift: a million dollars. That's great news. The library needs more money, and this will mean a lot.

Then there was more good news. The head librarian asked you to serve on a **staff** committee. Your job is to talk about using the money. You can't make a final decision. But you can make a **recommendation** to the **board of directors**. And the board usually does what committees like this **suggest**.

The committee has already met once. You learned about the gift. The **benefactor** wants the money used for one big thing, and she wants a fast decision. But she didn't say what to do. Then you talked about **procedures**. You agreed to meet again today and share your ideas.

At today's meeting, two people make **proposals**. One wants to add another room to the library for more books. And the other wants to spend the money on computers.

"We aren't very big," the first one says. "We can't do everything. Books are still the most important things in libraries. They always will

be, too. And this is the information age. So we need more books. But we can't get them without the new room."

"Sorry," says the other. "This isn't just the information age. It's also the **electronics** age. We need computers and Internet connections. That's better than books. People can use them for e-mail and research. People can get more information faster with computers. Let's get with it. Let's join the real world."

"Both ideas are good ones," says a third person. "But we can't work on both of them at once. Let's vote right now. Let's see which one we like most. Then we'll work on it."

Here's your challenge: Which idea will you vote for?

Life Skills Literacy:
Things to Know About Community Resources

Name_____ Date _____

Lesson 15: Information Resources

ACTIVITY PAGE

Word List

history	Internet	staff	suggest	proposal(s)
information	knowledge	recommendation	benefactor	electronics
librarian(s)	decision	board of directors	procedure(s)	

Increasing Your Understanding

1. Look at the word list in the box above. If you don't know a word, find out what it means. Try to figure it out from the way it is used on page 44. Or look it up in a dictionary.

2. Supply the missing word(s) in each of the sentences below. Use the word list above.

(a) Some people call this the _____ age, says the paragraph at the top of page 44.

(b) In the story on page 44, two people on the committee make _____.

(c) "This isn't just the information age," says the second person. "It's also the _____ age."

(d) Your committee can make a _____ to the _____.

(e) The _____ in the story wants the money used for one big thing.

Questions to Discuss

1. How do you answer the challenge on page 44? Is it easy to decide?

2. What are some resources you find in libraries? Brainstorm your answers.

3. What if there weren't any libraries? How would life change?

Things to Write About

1. Will there always be books? Or will we just use computers someday? Give your answer in a paragraph.

2. Can you get money for a library? Write a short letter to friends of the library. Ask them to make some donations. Tell them why the money is important.

Things to Do

1. Act out the story on page 44 with a partner. Imagine that you are both on the committee. Talk about some other ways a library could use a million dollars.

2. What other information resources can you use? Libraries are just one kind of possible resource. List at least six others.

3. Should schools use computers more? Imagine that you want to convince a school to get more computers for students to use. How will you do that? Work with two or three classmates and decide. Share your ideas with the class.

4. Find the libraries in your area. What are they? Who uses them? Share what you find with your class.

Life Skills Literacy:
Things to Know About Community Resources

Lesson 16: Money-Making Resources

Themes:

- Commercial resources
- Good and bad businesses

Background notes: The term "community resources" often brings to mind such shared and open entities as schools and parks, many supported by either government or nonprofit organizations. But profit-based institutions may also be resources of great communal value—as places for employment or shopping, for example. These pages introduce learners to that concept, and, through extension activities, ask them to consider what types of money-making enterprises are most important for, and useful to, local communities.

Preparation possibilities:

- <u>Think about</u>: Local money-making resources and business-based community efforts
- <u>Bring to class</u>: News stories showing local businesses as community resources; information about business-based efforts to assist your school

Technology resources:

- Search topics: *Convenience stores, corporate philanthropy*
- Web pages to try: Bell Atlantic Foundation (and similar organizations)

Student pages:

- Page 47 includes: An introduction to money-making resources; a dialogue between two friends about starting a convenience store

- Page 48 includes: A word list you may adjust for your class, and student activities

Especially for ESL: <u>Ask</u>: Are businesses in your first country a lot like businesses here? Do some of them make large profits? Do they share their profits by helping their communities?

Extra idioms and slang to introduce:

- *Go with the territory:* be a natural part of something
- *Crummy:* bad, cheap

Thoughts to share with learners: Capitalism is one kind of economic system. The United States, Canada, and many other countries are capitalistic. This means that private people own and run most businesses. But most countries don't have "pure" capitalism. Businesses can't just do anything they want. The government has a lot of laws about how they operate.

Questions to ask learners: What makes a business bad? What are some things bad businesses do? Do some people and businesses make too much money? Which ones? Should there be laws against that? Can a town or city exist without money-making resources? Why or why not?

Projects to assign learners: Find out what some businesses do for your community. Look in the newspapers. Or ask the businesses. Don't forget about the little things, like stores that let you put posters up so other people will see them. Share what you find with your class.

A fascinating fact to share: In the year that ended September 30, 1982, the American Telephone and Telegraph Company made a profit of $7.6 billion.

Lesson 16: Money-Making Resources

READING PAGE

Most nonprofit resources are good. Some of them help people for free. Many government resources are also good. They should be, because they belong to all of us. What about **commercial** resources? They can help people, too. But some help their owners most of all. Is this okay? Most people think so. **Businesses** need to make money. That's what they are for. If they are fair, everybody can win. **Customers** get the goods and services they want, and the businesses do well. What about bad businesses? That's another story. And the story isn't a good one.

Dialogue: The job

First Friend: Did I hear you right? You want to start a **convenience** store? On State Street?

Second Friend: Why not?

FF: Because the Quick-Trip Market is there. How many stores does that **neighborhood** need?

SF: Just one good one. But Quick-Trip Market isn't it. Their prices are awful, and their service is **terrible**.

FF: Besides, convenience stores are hard work. You have to **dedicate** your whole life to them.

SF: Not if you do things right. Once I get started I can hire some help. Then I can do something else myself. I might even start another store. Maybe someday I'll have a **chain**.

FF: You? Own a chain of stores? But you are so **idealistic**. I always thought you'd find a job helping people. Working for some nonprofit organization. Or maybe some **environmental** cause.

SF: But I will be helping people. Everybody needs food. If they can buy it close to home,

they won't have to drive so much. That will save gas and make the air better.

FF: Maybe. I suppose that's **capitalism**. That's how the **system** works.

SF: Of course it is. People work to make money, and there's nothing wrong with that. What's wrong is taking **advantage** of other people. That's what Quick-Trip does. It charges much too much. It's worse than no store at all. It can't make much money, either, because people hate it. But they'll like my store. It will be a real community resource.

FF: And you'll get rich.

SF: I don't think so. But if I do, I can thank this community. So I'll give some money back to it.

FF: My friend the philanthropist.

SF: Sounds good to me.

FF: It does to me, too. In fact, your whole **approach** sounds good. And I've saved a little money myself. Can I **invest** it in your store?

Life Skills Literacy:
Things to Know About Community Resources

Name_____ Date _____

Lesson 16: Money-Making Resources

ACTIVITY PAGE

Word List

commercial	convenience	dedicate	environmental	advantage
business(es)	neighborhood	chain	capitalism	approach
customer(s)	terrible	idealistic	system	invest

Increasing Your Understanding

1. Look at the word list in the box above. If you don't know a word, find out what it means. Try to figure it out from the way it is used on page 47. Or look it up in a dictionary.

2. Supply the missing word(s) in each of the sentences below. Use the word list above.

   (a) "What about _____ resources?" asks the paragraph at the top of page 47.

   (b) In the story on page 47, the first friend says the second friend is _____.

   (c) "I suppose that's _____," says the first friend. "That's how the _____ works."

   (d) At the story's end, the first friend thinks the second friend's whole _____ sounds good.

   (e) It's wrong to take _____ of other people, according to the second friend.

Questions to Discuss

1. Are convenience stores hard work? Is the first friend right in the story on page 47? Do owners have to dedicate a lot to their businesses?

2. Why do some stores charge a lot more than other stores for the same thing? Is this okay?

3. Is capitalism a good system? What's good about it? What's bad about it?

Things to Write About

1. Should businesses give money to their communities? Why or why not? Write your answer in a paragraph.

2. What kind of new money-making resources does your community need? Write two or three sentences about your ideas.

Things to Do

1. With a partner, act out the story on page 47. Talk about working in a convenience store. What's good about it? What's bad about it?

2. What resources make a good community? Imagine that you are going to move. What resources do you want your new community to have? List at least five.

3. Can you set up a good convenience store? Imagine that you and some friends are going to start a local convenience store. Work with two or three classmates to answer these questions. Where will the store be? What will its name be? What will it sell? Share your ideas with your class.

4. What are some good business resources in your area? Look around and decide. Imagine that some are closing. Which ones would your community miss most? Share your ideas with your class.

Lesson 17: Resources for Young People

TEACHER PAGE

Themes:

- Resources for all young people
- Resources for young people with special needs

Background notes: The young have always been among the most vulnerable members of society, so have always needed special community resources. But their need has grown in recent years as the nuclear family has become less stable, the extended family has dispersed geographically, and economic circumstances have forced more and more parents to leave their homes for work. These pages introduce learners to common resources for children, and use extension activities to invite exploration of local resources. You might also consider organizing a class tour of a local resource, particularly if you know of one searching for more volunteer assistance.

Preparation possibilities:

- Think about: Local community resources for young people; the need for more such resources
- Bring to class: News stories about local resources for young people; information about volunteering to assist in such resources

Technology resources:

- Search topics: *Special needs children, at-risk youth, education, day care*
- Web pages to try: Child Welfare League of America, Child Welfare League of Canada, Big Brothers Big Sisters (or similar child and youth organizations)

Student pages:

- Page 50 includes: An introduction to resources for special needs children and

at-risk youth; a story about roommates discussing ways to help children and youth

- Page 51 includes: A word list you may adjust for your class, and student activities

Especially for ESL: <u>Ask</u>: What community resources does your first country have for young people? Do young children go to day-care centers? Stay home?

Extra idioms and slang to introduce:

- *Lend a hand to someone:* help someone
- *Kid stuff:* something for children, not adults

Thoughts to share with learners: People of all skills can help the young. Teachers can teach, parents can feed and clothe, and carpenters can build playgrounds. Remember (from Lesson 6) what some people say: "It takes a village to raise a child."

Questions to ask learners: Who runs the resources for children in your area? The government? Nonprofit groups? Businesses? All of these? Who in the class likes working with children? What do you do with them? Do you get paid or do you volunteer? Can other students do the same thing?

Projects to assign learners: Visit a local resource for children. Find out if it needs volunteer help. Ask friends and family members what new resources your community needs. Share what you find with the class. List some of the community resources you used when you were younger.

A fascinating fact to share: Twenty percent of all American children under 18 live in poverty.

Lesson 17: Resources for Young People

Some children have **special needs**. That's what schools say. Maybe the kids are sick. Maybe they can't learn easily. And a lot of teens are **at risk**. Some are school **dropouts**. And some are homeless. These young people need extra help. Some cities have safe places for teens to live. And some have children's hospitals. There might be special houses near them. Families use them when children are sick. We have many resources for the young, but some places need more. Lots of kids still don't get enough help. What can we do about that?

Story: The helpers

"I can't believe it," said Sun. "Thanksgiving is coming in just two weeks."

"That **reminds** me to ask you all about **guests**," said Annie. "I'll be the chief cook. But I need to know how many people we're feeding."

The others promised to give her their lists very soon. Then Mara grew thoughtful. "We're really lucky, aren't we?" she said. "We have a lot to be thankful for."

"Yes," said Lenya. "But being thankful isn't enough. I want to do more to help other people."

"You can help me cook," **joked** Annie.

"I mean really. Like helping at-risk kids. Maybe I'll join Big Sisters, and be a **mentor** for a girl who needs help."

"That's a great idea," said Colin. "I was thinking of volunteering at the **Ronald McDonald** House downtown. That's where families stay when kids are in the hospital."

"Neat," said Sun. "Maybe we can all help kids next year. I might **tutor** some **refugees** who are new to this country. What about you, Mara?"

"Little kids aren't for me," said Mara. "I don't have the **patience** for them. I'll never have

a family. Besides, my job is **substance abuse** counseling. I already have some teen **clients**. But maybe I'll find another way to help adults next year."

There were lots of **opportunities** for volunteers, the roommates agreed.

Just then Tom came into the room. "Guess what?" he said. "My sister is coming for Thanksgiving. And she's bringing all seven kids! The youngest is two and the oldest is fourteen. Isn't that great?"

The others all looked at Mara.

"Don't worry about me. I can take kids for a day. But I'd better warn you. My own sister might bring five more. We may all be at risk by the end of the day."

Annie laughed. "Even if we aren't, the turkey will be," she said.

50

Life Skills Literacy:
Things to Know About Community Resources

Lesson 17: Resources for Young People

Word List

special needs	remind(s)	mentor	refugee(s)	abuse
at risk	guest(s)	Ronald McDonald	patience	client(s)
dropout(s)	joke(d)	tutor	substance	opportunities(y)

Increasing Your Understanding

1. Look at the word list in the box above. If you don't know a word, find out what it means. Try to figure it out from the way it is used on page 50. Or look it up in a dictionary.

2. Supply the missing word(s) in each of the sentences below. Use the word list above.

   (a) In the story on page 50, Mara says she doesn't have _____ for little kids.

   (b) Mara's job is _____ _____ counseling.

   (c) "You can help me cook," _____ Annie.

   (d) Some children have _____, according to the paragraph at the top of page 50.

   (e) A lot of teens are _____. Some are school _____.

Questions to Discuss

1. What does Mara mean at the end of the story on page 50?
2. How do you answer the question in the paragraph at the top of page 50?
3. What do you think of day care for young children? Is it a good resource? Or should more parents stay home with their children?

Things to Write About

1. Why do people say school dropouts are "at risk"? What does that mean? Is it true? Write your ideas in a paragraph.
2. How many community resources does page 50 talk about? Write a list.

Things to Do

1. Act out the story on page 50 with a partner. Take the parts of two roommates, but use your own names if you want. Talk about what you might do to help children.
2. Can you get volunteers to help children? Think of a good organization that helps children. It can be something from page 50 or something else. Make a poster or write a TV ad asking for help. Or make a drawing to use in a poster or TV ad.
3. What community resources do most children need? Imagine that you and two or three other students are starting a new city. Decide what resources it will have for children. Share your ideas with the class.
4. What are some community resources for young people in your area? Imagine that some are closing. Which ones would your community miss most? Share your ideas with your class.

Lesson 18: Counseling Resources

Themes:

- Family and other counselors
- Community resources for families
- Funding for community resources

Background notes: The world's population is close to six billion people. That means the world has almost six billion counselors in it. Most of us give advice to other people. And a surprising number of us are paid for our services in one way or another. These pages introduce learners to counseling services, particularly those available to families. Through extension activities, they lead to discussion of such subjects as how counseling works and fair payment for counseling services.

Preparation possibilities:

- Think about: Local family and counseling services of potential interest to your students
- Bring to class: Printed information about local counseling services, especially the most affordable

Technology resources:

- Search topics: *Family counselors, philanthropy*
- Web pages to try: International Association of Marriage and Family Counselors, United Way of America

Student pages:

- Page 53 includes: An introduction to counseling and family resources; a challenge story that also introduces the topic of nonprofit fund-raising activities
- Page 54 includes: A word list you may adjust for your class, and student activities

Especially for ESL: Ask: Do immigrants and refugees need special counseling services? What other resources do they need? What kinds of family resources does your first country have? What counseling services?

Extra idioms and slang to introduce:

- *Hit someone up:* ask for something
- *Psyched up:* excited about something

Thoughts to share with learners: The phone book is a good place to start looking for a counselor. Look under counselors, family services, and state and county mental health agencies. Family doctors and school personnel can also help. It is possible to see a counselor without spending a lot of money. Many in private practice and in nonprofit agencies charge on a sliding scale. People who see them pay what they can. And many insurance plans help pay for counselors.

Questions to ask learners: Who in the class might like to be a counselor? Who has counseled friends about problems? Why are counselors helpful? How do they work? What problems can they help solve? Who counsels other people as part of their work? Is it better to get advice from friends or from professional counselors?

Projects to assign learners: Look around your community for family resources. What can you find? What does your area need? What do you think? What do friends and family members think? Share your ideas with your class.

A fascinating fact to share: In the mid-1990s, United Way volunteers raised more than $3 billion a year in the United States.

Lesson 18: Counseling Resources

People say that "talk is cheap." But they aren't always right. Some people charge money for talking. Counselors and doctors are among them. They listen and talk for pay. They help clients solve problems. Can talk really help? It **certainly** can. It's a great way to get new ideas. You can find **certified** counselors in almost any town or city. Some of them **specialize**. One might work with families, for example. Another might work with children. How can you choose one? Ask around. Find out who has helped other people.

Challenge: Finding money

Community Fund Worker: Tell me about your idea.

Family Center Worker: Someday our new Family Center will offer all kinds of services. But we'll begin with just two. One is a day-care center. The other is family counseling.

CFW: I know this city needs more day-care centers. I've seen **statistics** showing that. But aren't lots of counselors **available** already?

FCW: Yes, but they're all in private practice. They can cost a lot. This city needs a nonprofit counseling service. We will charge on a **sliding scale**. People will pay what they can afford.

CFW: Will you work just with whole families? Or **individuals**? Or groups?

FCW: We'll do all kinds of counseling. But no heavy-duty **therapy**. If we can help solve problems, great. But we won't do much with major **depression** and things like that. We'll **refer** people who are very ill somewhere else. To a **psychiatrist**, for example. Lots of our work will be with kids and parents who can't get along.

CFW: I know what you mean. My own kids can be a real handful. Maybe I need one of your counselors.

FCW: Maybe. But we don't have any counselors yet. That's why I'm here. To carry out our **mission**, we need **fund-raising** help. Will the Community Fund support us? That would be easier than running our own fund drive.

CFW: It is easier. And this community supports us. The **media** are great to us. And we do very well **financially**. People like having just one major campaign a year to give to.

FCW: So can we count on the Fund to help us?

CFW: I can't answer that. One of our committees will decide. All I can do is make a recommendation. What more can you tell me to help make your case?

Here's your challenge: You be the Family Center Worker. How will you answer?

53   *Life Skills Literacy:*
Things to Know About Community Resources

Lesson 18: Counseling Resources

ACTIVITY
PAGE

Word List

certainly	statistic(s)	individual(s)	refer	fund-raising
certified(y)	available	therapy	psychiatrist	media
specialize	sliding scale	depression	mission	financially

Increasing Your Understanding

1. Look at the word list in the box above. If you don't know a word, find out what it means. Try to figure it out from the way it is used on page 53. Or look it up in a dictionary.

2. Supply the missing word(s) in each of the sentences below. Use the word list above.

    (a) "The _____ are great to us," says the Community Fund Worker in the story on page 53.

    (b) The Family Center won't do heavy-duty _____, according to the Center Worker.

    (c) _____ show that the city in the story needs more day-care centers.

    (d) The Family Center wants _____ help so it can carry out its _____.

    (e) Some counselors _____, according to the paragraph at the top of page 53.

Questions to Discuss

1. How do you answer the challenge on page 53? What kinds of information will help you get money?

2. How much money should counselors charge? Should they charge the same price to everybody? Should the ones in private practice charge more?

3. Is the Community Fund a good idea? Or should all nonprofit groups raise their own money?

Things to Write About

1. What makes a good counselor? Write your answer in a paragraph.

2. What's a good motto for a family center? Write two ideas.

Things to Do

1. With a partner, act out the story on page 53. Use your own names and words if you want.

2. How much should a nonprofit family center pay in expenses? The Better Business Bureau says a nonprofit should not spend more than 35 percent of its money in expenses. The rest should go to help people. What if a family center gets $150,000 in donations? What is the most it should use for expenses?

3. Think about family center finances. Imagine you and two or three other students are starting a family center like the one in the story. If you offer day care and counseling, what will you have to pay for? What other services will you add later? Will they cost money? Write down some of your ideas. Then share them with the class.

4. What kinds of counseling resources can you find in your area? Look around, try the phonebook, ask your doctor. Then share what you find with your class.

Life Skills Literacy:
Things to Know About Community Resources

Lesson 19: Resources for Older People

Themes:

- The needs of senior citizens
- Attitudes toward aging

Background notes: In 1995, people aged 65 and over were 12.8 percent of the U. S. population. In 2050, they are expected to be 20.4 percent of the population, according to the Census Bureau. Undoubtedly, resources for older people will become even more common than they are now. Just as certainly, seniors will become an even more important voice in politics. These pages introduce learners to a few resources now available, from discounted prices to Medicare. Through extension activities, they lead learners to explore and consider the resources available in their own areas.

Preparation possibilities:

- <u>Think about</u>: The number of senior citizens in your area
- <u>Bring to class</u>: Information about local resources for senior citizens, including Elderhostels

Technology resources:

- Search topics: *Elderly, senior services, Social Security, Medicare*
- Web pages to try: Facts on Medicare, American Association of Retired People, Elderhostels

Student pages:

- Page 56 includes: An introduction to the needs and interests of senior citizens; a dialogue in which two seniors discuss various aspects of aging
- Page 57 includes: A word list you may adjust for your class, and student activities

Especially for ESL: Some Americans don't treat senior citizens very well. But people in some other countries give the elderly great respect. <u>Ask</u>: How do people in your first country feel about seniors?

Extra idioms and slang to introduce:

- *Spring chicken:* a young person
- *Old as the hills:* very old

Thoughts to share with learners: Medicare is part of the Social Security system in the United States. It helps pay some medical bills of senior citizens. Some people think there should be resources like that for the whole population. The American Association for Retired People (AARP) is an organization that many older people belong to. It's an important resource for them. Elderhostel is a nonprofit organization that has programs all around the world for people aged 55 and older.

Questions to ask learners: Who in the class has volunteered or worked for pay in a program for senior citizens? Who likes working with older people? Why do older people vote more often than younger people do? What are the good things about growing older? What are the hard things about it?

Projects to assign learners: Visit a local resource for senior citizens. Find out what other resources seniors need to have in your area. Decide what you can do now to make your later life better. Then do it. Watch a TV show or movie with old people in it. What kinds of lives do the old people have? How are they treated? What special resources do they use? Share what you find with your class.

A fascinating fact to share: In 1998, Medicare paid for 28 percent of all hospital bills in the United States.

Lesson 19: Resources for Older People

Call them **senior** citizens. Call them **elderly**. Or call them old. But call them important, too. People live longer than they used to. So there are lots of older people in the United States and Canada. They vote more often than young people do. So they have a big part running the country. They help to get the special resources they need. These include **nursing homes** for the very old. But seniors want more than medical help. They want fun things to do. They want recreation and friends. They want to learn more. And they work to get all these things.

Dialogue: Growing older

First Friend: Can you come to my **retirement** party next month?

Second Friend: Sure. If you'll come to my birthday party the month after that. I'm turning 80, you know.

FF: Eighty? No way! Does that scare you to death?

SF: Of course not. If getting older scared people to death, we would all die young.

FF: I'm scared just of retirement. I don't know what I'll do with my time.

SF: The older I get the better life gets. You know what I did when I turned 75? I tried a **parachute** jump.

FF: Why would you do that?

SF: I wanted to see what it felt like. And it was wonderful!

FF: That really would scare me to death. There isn't much good I know about aging. We do get senior **discounts** for lots of stuff. And we can get government help from **Medicare**. But other things aren't so good. Some young people aren't very nice to seniors. And some companies **discriminate** against them.

SF: That's **ageism**. And it's stupid. But what do they know? Say, why don't you try an **Elderhostel**? Those are programs for people aged 55 or more. You go somewhere and learn something for a week or so. You might study **photography**, for example. That's a great retirement present to give yourself.

FF: Maybe. But I need to save my money. I might need to find a retirement community to live in. Some place with an **assisted** living building.

SF: Not me. I want to live near kids. We're all as young as we feel. And kids help me feel young.

FF: You look younger than 80. That's for sure.

SF: Thanks. But I can't wait to get there.

FF: Why?

SF: I'm getting a new **bowling** ball at Bryant's Sports Store. They're selling them for half price to 80-year-olds who want them for **personal** use. And I need one for the **tournament** next month.

56

Life Skills Literacy:
Things to Know About Community Resources

Lesson 19: Resources for Older People

ACTIVITY PAGE

Word List

senior	retirement	Medicare	Elderhostel	bowling
elderly	parachute	discriminate	photography	personal
nursing home(s)	discount(s)	ageism	assist(ed)	tournament

Increasing Your Understanding

1. Look at the word list in the box above. If you don't know a word, find out what it means. Try to figure it out from the way it is used on page 56. Or look it up in a dictionary.

2. Supply the missing word(s) in each of the sentences below. Use the word list above.

   (a) You can call older people _____ citizens, says the paragraph at the top of page 56.

   (b) The resources seniors need include _____ for the very old.

   (c) The second friend in the story on page 56 needs a new _____ ball for a _____.

   (d) The first friend talks about a retirement community with an _____ living building.

   (e) "We do get senior _____ for a lot of stuff," says the first friend.

Questions to Discuss

1. Do you agree with the second friend in the story on page 56? Are people only as old as they feel? What does "old" mean? What age are "old" people?

2. Are senior citizen discounts fair? Is it okay for younger people to pay more while older people pay less? How old should people be to get senior discounts?

3. Why do some people discriminate against seniors? What can be done to change this?

Things to Write About

1. What's the best age to be? Imagine that you have to be one age for about ten years. What age will you choose? Write your answer in a paragraph. Give reasons for your decision.

2. Get your drugstore to give senior discounts. Imagine that your local drugstore doesn't have special prices for older people. Tell the owner that it should. Write a letter saying

why. Also give the youngest age at which people should get the discount.

Things to Do

1. With a partner, act out the story on page 56. Use your own names and words if you want. Talk about why some people worry about getting old, but others don't.

2. What special things do most older people need? List at least six.

3. Plan a retirement community. Imagine that you and some friends are going to build a place where senior citizens can live in your community. What will it be like? Meet with two or three classmates and decide. Draw a map if you want. Then share your ideas with your class.

4. What kinds of resources for senior citizens does your town or city have? Look around and share what you find with your class.

Lesson 20: Self-help Resources

Themes:

- Self-help groups
- Alcoholics Anonymous and similar programs

Background notes: Logic suggests that the term "self-help group" could cover almost every human organization. Some people help themselves by belonging to these organizations. But convention reserves the term mostly for people working together to overcome personal, medical, psychological, and behavioral problems, such as drug and alcohol abuse. Even limited in this way, the term covers a lot of ground. An Internet search in the fall of 1998 disclosed a list of 300 such groups just in east central Illinois, their foci ranging from bereavement to addiction to stuttering. These pages will lead learners to consider the presence of such groups in their own communities, as well as to read about and discuss the general nature of the self-help movement and such components as Alcoholics Anonymous.

Preparation possibilities:

- <u>Think about</u>: Self-help groups in your area
- <u>Bring to class</u>: Newspaper and other listings of local self-help groups

Technology resources:

- Search topics: *Support groups, 12-step programs, self-help*
- Web pages to try: National Mental Health Consumers Self-Help Clearinghouse, Alcoholics Anonymous (and similar self-help groups)

Student pages:

- Page 59 includes: An introduction to self-help groups; a story about two friends involved in similar self-help programs
- Page 60 includes: A word list you may adjust for your class, and student activities

Especially for ESL: <u>Ask</u>: Are there many self-help groups in your first country? Are they like the groups here? Are there special self-help groups here for people whose first language isn't English?

Extra idioms and slang to introduce:

- *Lift yourself up by your own bootstraps:* help yourself
- *Fall off the wagon:* start drinking again, after stopping

Thoughts to share with learners: In "12-step programs" members take 12 steps to help solve their problems. Alcoholics Anonymous was the first such program. It started in 1935. In AA, members work to become sober. This means they recover, and stop using alcohol. But they say they are still alcoholics.

Questions to ask learners: What does "anonymous" mean? (That a person's name isn't known.) Why do the members of some self-help groups remain anonymous? Do you think that's a good idea? What are *self-improvement* programs? (The term usually refers to some kind of education.)

Projects to assign learners: Choose one kind of self-help group and find out more about it. Share what you learn.

A fascinating fact to share: Alcoholics Anonymous does not keep lists of people who join, so it doesn't know just how many members it has. In 1998, its worldwide estimate was 1,967,433.

Lesson 20: Self-help Resources

Self-help? Do you need community resources for that? Can't you do self-help alone? That's the idea, all right. But it doesn't always work. We can't do some things alone. We need other people to help. **Addiction** is one example. Some people can give up drugs by themselves. But most addicts can't. Who can help them? Ex-addicts often can. That's the **secret** of many self-help groups. People who share a problem help each other. They offer **mutual** support.

Story: "Something you should know"

"I'm glad you stopped by," said Angela. "Help yourself to a drink."

"No thanks," said Frank. "I can help myself by not helping myself. That's something you should know about me. I want to tell you before our **relationship** gets more serious. If it does, and I hope it will."

Angela smiled at him. "Don't you want a drink first?"

"That's what you need to know. I'm in **recovery**. I'm an **alcoholic**."

"That's funny."

"It is?"

"Not ha-ha funny. But I'm an alcoholic, too."

"Are you kidding? Then why are you offering drinks?"

"I'm thirsty. But all I've got is orange juice and root beer."

"So you're in recovery, too?"

"Yes. I went to a meeting last night. The **Alcoholics Anonymous** group downtown."

"I was at a meeting at my church."

"So that's one more thing we have in common. They say that **opposites** attract. But my best friends are a lot like me."

"Mine too. Maybe that's one reason **12-step programs** like **AA** work. They get **similar** people together to talk."

"The ones in my group aren't all that similar," Angela said. "Except for one thing. They don't **control** alcohol. It controls them. At least until they join AA. And that works **miracles** for some of them."

"It did for me. Strange as that seems."

"Why strange?"

"You'd think if two people with the same problem get together, the problem might get worse. But it doesn't. Not in this case, anyway."

"That's because these people share more than a problem. They share a commitment to solve it."

"Speaking of problems, do you smell something burning?"

"Oh no!" said Angela. "My dinner!"

She looked in the oven. "It's gone," she said. "Beyond help."

"Good," Frank told her. "There's another problem we can share. Let's go solve it together. I know a great place to eat."

"Let's go," said Angela.

Life Skills Literacy:
Things to Know About Community Resources

Lesson 20: Self-help Resources

Word List

addiction	relationship	Alcoholics Anonymous	AA	miracle(s)
secret	recovery	opposite(s)	similar	
mutual	alcoholic	12-step program(s)	control	

Increasing Your Understanding

1. Look at the word list in the box above. If you don't know a word, find out what it means. Try to figure it out from the way it is used on page 59. Or look it up in a dictionary.

2. Supply the missing word(s) in each of the sentences below. Use the word list above.

   (a) In the story on page 59, Frank says he is in a group called _____.

   (b) The people in Angela's group don't _____ alcohol, she says.

   (c) Programs like AA get _____ people together to talk, according to Frank.

   (d) People in self-help groups offer _____ support, says the paragraph at the top of page 59.

   (e) Sharing problems is the _____ of many self-help groups.

Questions to Discuss

1. What is the relationship of Angela and Frank in the story on page 59? How do you know?

2. Why do you think groups like AA are often successful? Can they help people who won't help themselves?

3. Could everybody use a self-help group of some kind? Does everybody have problems, or need support?

Things to Write About

1. Write a paragraph about a friend. How is the friend like you? How is the friend different from you? Are you friends because of your differences? Or your similarities?

2. What do you want to know? Write three questions using words from the list at the top of the page.

Things to Do

1. With a partner, act out the story on page 59. Use your own names and words if you want. Talk about why some people won't join self-help groups.

2. What kinds of self-help groups are there? List at least five.

3. Does your community have trouble with drugs and alcohol? What should be done? Meet with two or three classmates and talk about your ideas. Then share some of them with your class.

4. Does your community have lots of resources for people with problems? Look around and find out what some of them are. Share what you find with your class.

Lesson 21: Natural Resources

Themes:

- Public and private use of natural resources

Background notes: The subject of natural resources offers an excellent focal point for considering private and public ownership of community resources. Not that the discussion then becomes easy—it usually does not. We may quickly decide that we all must share air. But the best use of land with both commercial and recreational potential is a topic sure to evoke much diverse and often strong opinion. These pages invite your learners to join the debate about one fictional piece of land, then explore, through discussion and other activities, more general questions about the natural resources of various communities.

Preparation possibilities:

- Think about: Local controversy about the best use of land or other natural resources
- Bring to class: Information about local resources with commercial and recreational potential

Technology resources:

- Search topics: *National parks, natural resources*
- Web pages to try: National Park Service (U.S.), Natural Resources Canada

Student pages:

- Page 62 includes: An introduction to natural resources and ownership of them; a challenge story about the best use of state land with both commercial and recreational potential
- Page 63 includes: A word list you may adjust for your class, and student activities

Especially for ESL: Ask: Who owns most natural resources in your first country?

Extra idioms and slang to introduce:

- *Strike it rich:* get rich suddenly (as if by striking gold)
- *Donnybrook:* a big argument or fight

Thoughts to share with learners: The ownership of natural resources is different in different economic systems. Private people and companies own most resources in the "capitalist" system. The government owns most resources in a "socialist" or "communist" system. Remember that things can be community resources even if they are privately owned. (See Lesson 16, "Money-Making Resources.") Governments at many different levels run parks. In some places you have a choice of national, state or provincial, and local parks to visit.

Questions to ask learners: What natural resources are also community resources? Is it okay for one person or company to own a whole lake? A whole mountain? How does the government control natural resources that it doesn't own? Is doing that a good idea?

Projects to assign learners: Visit a local park you have never gone to before. Think of a way to make it a better place, and do it. Learn more about a natural resource in your area. Look around your community. Do you see private resources you think should be public? The opposite? Share your ideas with your class.

A fascinating fact to share: On summer days in the late 1990s, 6,500 cars a day went to Grand Canyon National Park. But the park had only 2,400 parking spaces.

Lesson 21: Natural Resources

Who owns the air? Nobody. What about other natural resources? What about land? Some land is private. But a lot is public. That means we all own it. But it doesn't mean we agree about it. There are many ways to use public land. Some people want a lot of parks, and others want more wild land. Some want to sell most government land for commercial use. Is there public land in your community? If there is, you can be sure of one thing. People disagree about how it should be used.

Challenge: A decision to make

You have a hard decision to make.

Your state has many square miles of wild land. For years, the government has **leased** the land to **lumber** companies. The companies cut the trees on the land and sell it. But some people say the land should be a park. They have started a **petition** drive asking for that.

Some of your friends support the drive. And they want your help.

"This is **spectacular** land," they say. "Everybody should have **access** to it. Not just the lumber companies. Besides, they are destroying the land. You can't replace those huge old trees they are cutting down."

Your family doesn't agree. "That's **ridiculous**," your father says. "We already have too many parks. What we don't have is enough jobs. And we don't have a very good economy right now."

You aren't so sure he's right. So you **repeat** what your friends tell you. "The land belongs to everybody," you say. "Everybody can use it if it's a park."

"The economy belongs to everybody, too," your father says. "And if there aren't enough jobs

we're all going to **suffer**. Recreation is important. I know that. But jobs are a whole lot more important. People who don't have jobs might have time to play, but they don't have any money. They can't use fancy new state parks."

Now you're confused. You think both **arguments** sound good. Then your father surprises you. "I'm going to fight that park," he says. "I'm going to start my own petition drive. I'll fight fire with fire. In a democracy, the people are always right. And the people will agree with me if I give them a chance. I'll do that, too, but I need a whole lot of help from you."

Here's your challenge: What will you do? Which side will you help?

Life Skills Literacy:
Things to Know About Community Resources

Name _____   Date _____

Lesson 21: Natural Resources

Word List

entrance	vehicle	lumber	access	suffer
fee(s)	campsite	petition	ridiculous	argument(s)
per	lease(d)	spectacular	repeat	

Increasing Your Understanding

1. Look at the word list in the box above. If you don't know a word, find out what it means. Try to figure it out from the way it is used on page 62. Or look it up in a dictionary.

2. Supply the missing word in each of the sentences below. Use the word list above.

   (a) The sign at the top of page 62 lists entrance _____ for a park.

   (b) The price for a _____ is $12 for one night.

   (c) You think both _____ sound good in the story on page 62.

   (d) Your father says people will _____ if there aren't enough jobs.

   (e) People who want a park have started a _____ drive to get it.

Questions to Discuss

1. How do you answer the challenge on page 62? What other information could help you decide?

2. Is the whole earth a community resource? Should all land be public? Or should it all be private?

3. Should rich countries help poor countries? Some countries have lots of natural resources, so they are rich. Some countries are the opposite. Is this fair?

Things to Write About

1. Write a paragraph about an important natural resource in your community.

2. Write a letter to the newspaper about a park in your area. Talk about something that could make it better.

Things to Do

1. With a partner, act out the parts of two people in the story on page 62. Use your own names and words if you want. Talk about good parks you have seen.

2. Do the math: Imagine that you visit the park in the drawing on page 62. You are with two friends in one car. How much does it cost to visit for a day? What if you had an annual pass for your car and for each of you? How much would that cost? How many one-day visits can you make and still spend less than that?

3. Can you get people to agree with you? Imagine that you get a chance to vote on the park in the story on page 62. Will you support it? Work against it? Meet with two or three classmates and decide. Then make a TV ad asking people to vote your way. Act out your ad for the class.

4. Look around your community. What are its best natural resources? Make a list and share it with your class.

Life Skills Literacy:
Things to Know About Community Resources

Lesson 22: Art Resources

Themes:

- Community art resources
- Ownership and control of art

Background notes: Some people believe that cities—or even countries—are as good as their arts. Others think little about them. These pages lead learners first to consider some general aspects of art, then to explore the arts resources of their own communities. They focus primarily on visual arts, but you can easily extend discussions and explorations to other areas. You may wish to consider organizing a class visit to a museum or other resource.

Preparation possibilities:

- <u>Think about</u>: Public and private art resources in your area
- <u>Bring to class</u>: Information about local museums; news stories about art in your community
- <u>Invite to class</u>: A local artist or art authority—possibly a critic or museum representative

Technology resources:

- Search topics: *Art, architecture, museums*
- Web pages to try: Smithsonian Institution (and others by name), Canadian Heritage Information Network, Museums Index

Student pages:

- Page 65 includes: An introduction to art and its ownership; a dialogue between two student artists
- Page 66 includes: A word list you may adjust for your class, and student activities

Especially for ESL: <u>Ask</u>: What community art resources does your first country have?

Extra idioms and slang to introduce:

- *Make a name for yourself:* become well known
- *Take a shot at something:* try something

Thoughts to share with learners: The question of who owns and controls art can get very complicated. If you own a painting or a sculpture, you can decide who sees it. And if you write a book you can keep people from copying it for a certain number of years. But after that, it enters the "public domain." That means anybody can copy it and sell it.

Questions to ask learners: Why are community art resources important? Who should pay for them? Should all public museums have times when you can get in without paying? Why or why not? What if you create something for the company where you work? Who owns it? (Usually the company does.) Do you agree with this idea? Television, radio, the Internet, libraries, and other such things make it easier for everybody to enjoy the arts than ever before. Why do some people spend many years collecting art, then give it all away? Could you do that?

Projects to assign learners: Make a list of community art resources you see everyday. Look for them carefully on your way to school or work.

A fascinating fact to share: Claude Monet, a famous French painter, lived from 1840 to 1926. He got to spend much of his time painting after he won a lottery in 1891.

Name_____ Date_____

Lesson 22: Art Resources

Who owns art? Whoever **creates** it owns it first. Whoever buys it owns it next. If that's a museum, a lot of people are lucky. They don't need to own the art. It's a community resource. Everybody who visits the museum can enjoy it. But all art isn't in buildings. **Sculpture**, for example, is often outside. And buildings themselves can be art. If their **architecture** is good, they are a real **asset** to their community. They are a kind of public art. Everybody can appreciate them.

Dialogue: Art on the street

First Student Artist: What are you doing after graduation?

Second Student Artist: I'm going to rent a **studio** and paint **landscapes**.

FSA: Can you make enough to survive?

SSA: I'll try it for a year. I have a friend with a **gallery**, and she's promised to show my work. So at least I'll get some **exposure**.

FSA: You might do very well. I know you've got a lot of **talent**.

SSA: Thanks. So do you. You paint great **portraits**. Is that what you'll be doing in June?

FSA: At least for the summer, yes.

SSA: Want to share my studio?

FSA: No thanks. The streets will be my studio.

SSA: You're kidding! You're going to be a street artist? You'll get more exposure than I will.

FSA: That's for sure. Exposure to rain and snow and everything else. But the summer won't be too bad. And I like working outdoors.

SSA: Not me. That's why I do my landscapes from photos. Have you tried street work before?

FSA: Last summer I set up in Lincoln Park.

SSA: How did it go?

FSA: Great. I made the newspaper the first day. And I got a bank **commission** the second day.

SSA: A bank commission? Wow! That's great! Tell me about it.

FSA: The bank was across the street from the park. The first day I was there there was a holdup, and the **robber** ran right past me. A **reporter** talked to me and put me in the paper. That's how the bank got my name. Then they offered money for a portrait of the robber.

SSA: Did you do it?

FSA: Yes. It didn't help much, because he had a **mask** on. But the bank still paid.

SSA: That's great. If I start to go broke in my studio, maybe I can find some robbers to paint!

65

Life Skills Literacy:
Things to Know About Community Resources

Lesson 22: Art Resources

ACTIVITY PAGE

Word List

create(s)	asset	gallery	portrait(s)	reporter
sculpture	studio	exposure	commission	mask
architecture	landscape(s)	talent	robber	

Increasing Your Understanding

1. Look at the word list in the box above. If you don't know a word, find out what it means. Try to figure it out from the way it is used on page 65. Or look it up in a dictionary.

2. Supply the missing word(s) in each of the sentences below. Use the word list above.

   (a) The first student artist paints great _____, says the second artist in the story on page 65.

   (b) The first artist's painting didn't help much, because the robber wore a _____.

   (c) The second student artist's friend has a _____ that shows artwork.

   (d) Whoever _____ art owns it first, says the paragraph at the top of page 65.

   (e) Buildings with good _____ are a real _____ to their community.

Questions to Discuss

1. Do you think the artists in the story on page 65 will be successful? What does it mean to be a successful artist?

2. What kind of art resources should a good city have? Think about art you can hear and read, not just art you can see. Brainstorm your answers.

3. Who should control the outdoor art in a community? What if a home owner puts up a big outdoor statue that nobody else likes? Is that okay?

Things to Write About

1. Write a paragraph about some public art you like. It might be a statue or a building with good architecture.

2. What kind of painting do you want? Write a letter to an artist. Tell him or her you want to commission a painting. Describe the picture and ask for a price.

Things to Do

1. Act out the story on page 65 with a partner. Use your own names and words if you want. Talk about some art you like.

2. What kinds of art can you think of? List at least seven. Underline the two you like most.

3. What kind of art does your community need? Talk about that with two or three other students. Then share your ideas with your class.

4. Find some free art in your community. Where can you go to see it or hear it? Share what you find with your class.

Lesson 23: Sports Resources

Themes:

- The need for physical activity
- Sports for spectators and participants

Background notes: Sports resources are critically important to many people—participants and spectators alike. So much so that sports are major industries in the United States, Canada, and numerous other countries. These pages introduce learners to the importance of physical exercise and to community sports facilities as one source of such exercise—and of spectator pleasure. Discussion and other extension activities ask learners to consider the place of sports in their own communities and lives.

Preparation possibilities:

- Think about: Sports resources in your area
- Bring to class: Descriptions of school and other sports programs open to your students

Technology resources:

- Search topics: *Sports, athletics, sport statistics*
- Web pages to try: Sports On-line, The Sporting News

Student pages:

- Page 68 includes: An introduction to the need for physical activity; a story about friends helping to create new community sports resources
- Page 69 includes: A word list you may adjust for your class, and student activities

Especially for ESL: Ask: What are the favorite sports in your first country? Do lots of people play them? Are there both professional and amateur players? Do most communities have good sports resources?

Extra idioms and slang to introduce:

- *Work up a sweat:* get some exercise
- *Couch potato:* somebody who watches a lot of television

Thoughts to share with learners: People mean different things when they talk about "sports." Sometimes they mean very athletic and competitive games. Sometime they mean almost any kind of recreation. The story on page 68 shows that people can get exercise from sports in different ways. One, of course, is to play the sport. Another is to help build sports resources. There are many kinds of sports resources, not just playing fields. Think about newspaper sports pages, for example, or TV shows.

Questions to ask learners: What kinds of sports resources does your community have? What kinds does it need? How important are sports to you? What kinds of jobs can you get working with sports? What level of sports do you like to watch best—professional? high school? college?

Projects to assign learners: Try a sport you have never tried before. Watch a sport you have never seen before. Share what you do and see with your class. Ask some friends and family members what they think about the way professional athletes are paid. Is it too much? Just right?

A fascinating fact to share: The 1998 Super Bowl was seen on television in 800 million households in 144 countries. Attending the game cost an average price of about $275.

Lesson 23: Sports Resources

READING PAGE

Years ago, most people lived and worked on farms. Now more people work indoors. They have **sedentary** lives. They don't get the **activity** they need for good health. So they have to find ways to **exercise**. That's why sports and games are important. And that's why cities and towns need good playing fields. They give everyone a chance to get out and work out. The people who use them often feel better. They also have a lot of fun. And the fun doesn't cost much money.

Story: Working out

"Hey guys," Lenya said to her roommates. "What are you all doing Saturday?"

Sun, Annie, and Mara said they were free. Colin was going to be away.

"What about you, Tom?" Lenya asked.

"It's a sports day for me," Tom told her. "You won't believe how full my **schedule** is."

"Don't you mean the TV schedule?" asked Sun. "You aren't actually going to **participate** in athletics, are you?"

"Not me. It's TV sports for me. You know me. I'm a world-class **spectator**."

"You can say that again," said Lenya. "How about joining me on the playing fields Saturday? I can use all of you."

Tom looked doubtful. "What are we playing? **Soccer**? Softball?"

"We won't be playing. We'll be working. But we'll also be having fun."

Now Tom looked really doubtful.

"Tell us more," he said.

"I'm a member of the All-City Sports Club, remember? And we're building a new ball field for the city in Woodville Park. It's all volunteer **labor**, and I can sure use some of yours this weekend. There's a big free **barbecue** in the afternoon for everyone who helps."

"Count me in," said Sun.

"Me too," said Annie and Mara.

"I don't know," said Tom. "I'm not too big on **physical** labor." Then he smiled. "But I am too big around the waist. Maybe this **project** could help."

"Of course it will," said Mara. "It could be fun, too. And if we all eat there, I won't have to cook that night."

"You're such a sports **enthusiast**, Tom," said Sun. "Aren't you excited about having more **amateur** games at the park?"

"Okay," said Tom. "I'm convinced. I'll come—on one **condition**."

"What?" asked Lenya.

"I want to bring my **portable** TV for the afternoon game."

Lenya laughed. "You may be a hopeless case," she said. "But sure. Bring it along."

Lesson 23: Sports Resources

ACTIVITY PAGE

Word List

sedentary	schedule	soccer	physical	amateur
activity	participate	labor	project	condition
exercise	spectator	barbecue	enthusiast	portable

Increasing Your Understanding

1. Look at the word list in the box above. If you don't know a word, find out what it means. Try to figure it out from the way it is used on page 68. Or look it up in a dictionary.

2. Supply the missing word in each of the sentences below. Use the word list above.

   (a) In the story on page 68, Tom says he's a world-class _____.

   (b) "You won't believe how full my _____ is," he tells his friends.

   (c) There's a free _____ on Saturday for people who help, according to Lenya.

   (d) Many people live _____ lives, says the paragraph at the top of page 68.

   (e) People don't get the _____ they need for good health, the paragraph says.

Questions to Discuss

1. Why is Tom doubtful in the story on page 68?
2. Which is more important for a community—professional sports, or amateur sports?
3. Why do some professional athletes in America get paid so much? Do they get paid too much?

Things to Write About

1. What sports do you like? Write a paragraph about one of them.
2. What are some benefits of exercise? Write about two benefits.

Things to Do

1. With a partner, act out the parts of two people in the story on page 68. Do you think Tom will have a good time on Saturday?
2. What things make a person a good athlete? List at least five.
3. Plan a new park for your community. Work with two or three other students. Where will the park be? What will it be like? What kinds of sports resources will it have? Share your ideas with the class.
4. What amateur sports resources does your community have? Look around and share what you find with the class.

Lesson 24: Community Theater Resources

Themes:

- Community theater
- Watching and participating in professional and amateur theater

Background notes: Movies may come, and television too, together with dire prediction of theater's demise. But live stagecraft survives, and even thrives in many communities. So it should, because, like sports, theater is a resource for both participants and spectators. These pages invite learners to weigh the part that theater plays in their own lives and communities. Extension activities invite them to consider why theater remains so important despite competing forms of entertainment, and to find ways to support it in their own schools, towns, and cities.

Preparation possibilities:

- <u>Think about</u>: Theatrical resources in your area
- <u>Bring to class</u>: Notices of school and local performances

Technology resources:

- Search topics: *Theater, community theater, youth theater*
- Web pages to try: The School Show Page, Encyclopedia of Canadian Theater

Student pages:

- Page 71 includes: An introduction to theater; a challenge story about two friends discussing the best kind of theater to direct
- Page 72 includes: A word list you may adjust for your class, and student activities

Especially for ESL: <u>Ask</u>: What entertainment resources does your first country have? Does your new country have plays and other entertainment in your first language?

Extra idioms and slang to introduce:

- *Ham:* a bad actor; somebody who overacts
- *Hit:* a successful play

Thoughts to share with learners: Many communities have different kinds of theaters. Some are in schools and colleges. Some are community theaters for amateurs. And some are for professionals. Theaters are like sports—you can enjoy seeing them or being part of them. Musical groups are like this, too.

Questions to ask learners: What kinds of plays do you like best? Musicals? Mysteries? Something else? Who in the class is an actor? Who has worked with a theater? Which is better, to watch a play or to be in it? What are the differences between watching TV and going to live theater? Will there always be live theater? William Shakespeare said that "all the world's a stage." What did he mean? Do you agree?

Projects to assign learners: Go to a play and tell the class about it. Sign up to be in or help with a school or community play. Find newspaper stories about local theaters and bring them to class. Think about the entertainment resources in your community. What more would be good? (See also Number 3 of "Things to do" on page 72.)

A fascinating fact to share: The largest theater on Broadway in New York has 1,933 seats. Australia has the largest theater in the world. It seats 8,003. The Coliseum amphitheater in Rome, Italy, has room for 87,000 people.

Name_____ Date_____

Lesson 24: Community Theater Resources

 READING PAGE

When a **theater** gives a play, where's the best place to be? Some people think it's on the **stage**. They like to sing and act and dance. Others want to help offstage. They don't want to **perform**. But they might be on the **crew** and help build the **set**. Or they might do lighting, or help with **publicity**. Some people don't want to work on the play at all. They just want to see it. They want to be in the **audience**. That's okay, too. Theaters have good places for just about everyone.

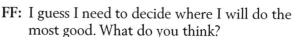

Challenge: The next job

First Friend: I've got a problem.

Second Friend: I hear you're looking for work.

FF: I was. But now I've got two job offers.

SF: A lot of people would like that problem.

FF: I know. But both jobs are good and I can't decide.

SF: Are both of them in theater?

FF: Yes. Both are for **directors**. One's a professional company that travels a lot.

SF: Right down the road to **fame** and fortune, I hope. That sounds great. But what's the other one?

FF: It's with the community theater here in town.

SF: Go with the pros. That's where the money is. And you get to direct real **actors** and **actresses**. Not a bunch of **stagestruck** amateurs. Go on the road. That's your chance to make it big. I'll miss you, but you've got some real talent. Don't waste it on community theater.

FF: But that isn't wasting it.

SF: Oh, right. In community theater, just about anybody gets to do something, even if they don't know a thing and aren't any good.

FF: That's what's fun about it. You take people with no experience at all and put them in a theater. At first they're scared to death. But they get better at every **rehearsal**. And then they come alive, and **magic** happens. You should see their faces the first time they hear the **applause**. That's why I cry on every opening night.

SF: Doesn't magic happen with professional theater, too?

FF: Yes. Especially when we go into schools. I love that. And I like to travel, too.

SF: So how will you make your choice?

FF: I guess I need to decide where I will do the most good. What do you think?

> **Here's your challenge:** Decide what the first friend should do.

71

Life Skills Literacy:
Things to Know About Community Resources

Lesson 24: Community Theater Resources

ACTIVITY
PAGE

Word List

theater	crew	audience	actor(s)	rehearsal
stage	set	director(s)	actress(es)	magic
perform	publicity	fame	stagestruck	applause

Increasing Your Understanding

1. Look at the word list in the box above. If you don't know a word, find out what it means. Try to figure it out from the way it is used on page 71. Or look it up in a dictionary.

2. Supply the missing word(s) in each of the sentences below. Use the word list above.

  (a) The paragraph at the top of page 71 talks about the best place to be in a _____.

  (b) Some people want to be in the _____, and that's okay.

  (c) People on the _____ help build the _____.

  (d) The second friend in the story on page 71 talks about _____ amateur actors.

  (e) Amateurs get better at every _____, the first friend says. Then _____ happens.

Questions to Discuss

1. How do you answer the challenge on page 71? What's the best community resource—professional theater or community theater?

2. Is the first friend right? Can magic happen in theaters? What does that mean?

3. Should every large town or city have a place for live theater? Who should pay for it?

Things to Write About

1. What do you like best? Plays? Movies? TV shows? Write a paragraph saying why.

2. What kind of people make good actors and actresses? Write two or three of your ideas.

Things to Do

1. Act out the story on page 71 with a partner. Talk about a good play or TV show you have seen.

2. Make a drawing to go with the story on page 71.

3. Plan a perfect city. What kinds of entertainment should it have? Work with two or three other students. Make a list of your answers, and share them with the class.

4. What theater resources does your community have? Which are for amateurs? Which are for professionals? Look around and share what you find with the class.

Slang and Idioms Used in This Book

Answers

Words for Completing Sentences:

Page 3: (a) in common; (b) island; (c) governments; (d) spider; (e) connect

Page 6: (a) symbol; (b) bureaucracy; (c) executive, legislative, judiciary; (d) diagram; (e) jurisdiction

Page 9: (a) philanthropists; (b) cause; (c) charities; (d) taxes; (e) funds

Page 12: (a) include; (b) announce; (c) emergencies; (d) lecture; (e) initiative

Page 15: (a) contribute; (b) democracy; (c) allegiance; (d) politics; (e) demolish, parking garage

Page 18: (a) mandatory; (b) attitude; (c) appreciate; (d) village; (e) volunteers

Page 21: (a) welfare; (b) heading; (c) listing, legal; (d) unemployment; (e) poverty, paycheck

Page 24: (a) toll-free; (b) appointment; (c) apply; (d) social worker; (e) vocational

Page 27: (a) Immigration, Naturalization; (b) applications; (c) Congress; (d) Registration; (e) Aliens

Page 30: (a) referendum; (b) campaign; (c) entertainment; (d) colleges, universities; (e) elementary

Page 33: (a) small claims court; (b) defendant; (c) represented, lawyer; (d) criminal; (e) arranged

Page 36: (a) economy; (b) advancement; (c) motto; (d) contacts; (e) accurately

Page 39: (a) cadet; (b) regular; (c) excitement; (d) disasters; (e) allergic

Page 42: (a) informed; (b) reform; (c) brutality; (d) local; (e) common

Page 45: (a) information; (b) proposals; (c) electronics; (d) recommendation, board of directors; (e) benefactor

Page 48: (a) commercial; (b) idealistic; (c) capitalism, system; (d) approach; (e) advantage

Page 51: (a) patience; (b) substance, abuse; (c) joked; (d) special needs; (e) at risk, dropouts

Page 54: (a) media; (b) therapy; (c) statistics; (d) fund-raising, mission; (e) specialize

Page 57: (a) senior; (b) nursing homes; (c) bowling, tournament; (d) assisted; (e) discounts

Page 60: (a) Alcoholics Anonymous; (b) control; (c) similar; (d) mutual; (e) secret

Page 63: (a) fees; (b) campsite; (c) arguments; (d) suffer; (e) petition

Page 66: (a) portraits; (b) mask; (c) gallery; (d) creates; (e) architecture, asset

Page 69: (a) spectator; (b) schedule; (c) barbecue; (d) sedentary; (e) exercise

Page 72: (a) theater; (b) audience; (c) crew, set; (d) stagestruck; (e) rehearsal, magic

Math Problems

Page 18: Number 2 under "Things to do": four years

Page 36: Number 2 under "Things to do": $80; $4,160; $124,800

Page 54: Number 2 under "Things to do": $52,500

Page 63: Number 2 under "Things to do": $14 for a day; $75 with an annual pass; five visits (which would cost $70)

Share Your Bright Ideas with Us!

We want to hear from you! Your valuable comments and suggestions will help us meet your current and future classroom needs.

Your name_____Date_____

School name_____Phone_____

School address_____

Grade level taught_____Subject area(s) taught_____Average class size_____

Where did you purchase this publication?_____

Was your salesperson knowledgeable about this product?   Yes_____   No_____

What monies were used to purchase this product?

____School supplemental budget   ____Federal/state funding   ____Personal

Please "grade" this Walch publication according to the following criteria:

Quality of service you received when purchasing	A	B	C	D	F
Ease of use	A	B	C	D	F
Quality of content	A	B	C	D	F
Page layout	A	B	C	D	F
Organization of material	A	B	C	D	F
Suitability for grade level	A	B	C	D	F
Instructional value	A	B	C	D	F

COMMENTS:_____

_____

What specific supplemental materials would help you meet your current—or future—instructional needs?

_____

Have you used other Walch publications? If so, which ones?_____

May we use your comments in upcoming communications?   ____Yes   ____No

Please **FAX** this completed form to **207-772-3105**, or mail it to:

Product Development, J. Weston Walch, Publisher, P.O. Box 658, Portland, ME 04104-0658

We will send you a **FREE GIFT** as our way of thanking you for your feedback. **THANK YOU!**